Spiral to Infinity Steve Allen

"Fractal images are often made up of small images-within-images, constantly
repeating and going smaller and smaller."– **Steve Allen**

D1364210

Investigations
IN NUMBER, DATA, AND SPACE®

GRADE

1

Number Games and Crayon Puzzles

Addition, Subtraction, and the Number System 3   UNIT 6

Glenview, Illinois • Boston, Massachusetts
Chandler, Arizona • Upper Saddle River, New Jersey

The Investigations curriculum was developed by TERC, Cambridge, MA.

T E R C

This material is based on work supported by the National Science Foundation ("NSF") under Grant No. ESI-0095450. Any opinions, findings, and conclusions or recommendations expressed in this material are those of the author(s) and do not necessarily reflect the views of the National Science Foundation.

ISBN-13: 978-0-328-60007-6

ISBN-10: 0-328-60007-5

1 2 3 4 5 6 7 8 9 10 V003 14 13 12 11 10

T E R C

Co-Principal Investigators

Susan Jo Russell

Karen Economopoulos

Authors

Lucy Wittenberg
Director Grades 3–5

Karen Economopoulos
Director Grades K–2

Virginia Bastable
(SummerMath for Teachers,
Mt. Holyoke College)

Katie Hickey Bloomfield

Keith Cochran

Darrell Earnest

Arusha Hollister

Nancy Horowitz

Erin Leidl

Megan Murray

Young Oh

Beth W. Perry

Susan Jo Russell

Deborah Schifter
(Education
Development Center)

Kathy Sillman

Administrative Staff

Amy Taber
Project Manager

Beth Bergeron

Lorraine Brooks

Emi Fujiwara

Contributing Authors

Denise Baumann

Jennifer DiBrienza

Hollee Freeman

Paula Hooper

Jan Mokros

Stephen Monk
(University of Washington)

Mary Beth O'Connor

Judy Storeygard

Cornelia Tierney

Elizabeth Van Cleef

Carol Wright

Technology

Jim Hammerman

Classroom Field Work

Amy Appell

Rachel E. Davis

Traci Higgins

Julia Thompson

Collaborating Teachers

This group of dedicated teachers carried out extensive field testing in their classrooms, met regularly to discuss issues of teaching and learning mathematics, provided feedback to staff, welcomed staff into their classrooms to document students' work, and contributed both suggestions and written material that has been incorporated into the curriculum.

Bethany Altchek

Linda Amaral

Kimberly Beauregard

Barbara Bernard

Nancy Buell

Rose Christiansen

Chris Colbath-Hess

Lisette Colon

Kim Cook

Frances Cooper

Kathleen Drew

Rebeka Eston Salemi

Thomas Fisher

Michael Flynn

Holly Ghazey

Susan Gillis

Danielle Harrington

Elaine Herzog

Francine Hiller

Kirsten Lee Howard

Liliana Klass

Leslie Kramer

Melissa Lee Andrichak

Kelley Lee Sadowski

Jennifer Levitan

Mary Lou LoVecchio

Kristen McEnaney

Maura McGrail

Kathe Millett

Florence Molyneaux

Amy Monkiewicz

Elizabeth Monopoli

Carol Murray

Robyn Musser

Christine Norrman

Deborah O'Brien

Timothy O'Connor

Anne Marie O'Reilly

Mark Paige

Margaret Riddle

Karen Schweitzer

Elisabeth Seyferth

Susan Smith

Debra Sorvillo

Shoshanah Starr

Janice Szymaszek

Karen Tobin

JoAnn Trauschke

Ana Vaisenstein

Yvonne Watson

Michelle Woods

Mary Wright

Note: Unless otherwise noted, all contributors listed above were staff of the Education Research Collaborative at TERC during their work on the curriculum. Other affiliations during the time of development are listed.

Advisors

Deborah Lowenberg Ball,
University of Michigan

Hyman Bass, Professor of Mathematics and Mathematics Education
University of Michigan

Mary Canner, Principal, Natick Public Schools

Thomas Carpenter, Professor of Curriculum and Instruction,
University of Wisconsin-Madison

Janis Freckmann, Elementary Mathematics Coordinator,
Milwaukee Public Schools

Lynne Godfrey, Mathematics Coach,
Cambridge Public Schools

Ginger Hanlon, Instructional Specialist in Mathematics,
New York City Public Schools

DeAnn Huinker, Director, Center for Mathematics and
Science Education Research, University of Wisconsin-Milwaukee

James Kaput, Professor of Mathematics, University of
Massachusetts-Dartmouth

Kate Kline, Associate Professor, Department of Mathematics
and Statistics, Western Michigan University

Jim Lewis, Professor of Mathematics,
University of Nebraska-Lincoln

William McCallum, Professor of Mathematics,
University of Arizona

Harriet Pollatsek, Professor of Mathematics,
Mount Holyoke College

Debra Shein-Gerson, Elementary Mathematics Specialist,
Weston Public Schools

Gary Shevell, Assistant Principal,
New York City Public Schools

Liz Sweeney, Elementary Math Department,
Boston Public Schools

Lucy West, Consultant, Metamorphosis:
Teaching Learning Communities, Inc.

This revision of the curriculum was built on the work of the many authors who contributed to the first edition (published between 1994 and 1998). We acknowledge the critical contributions of these authors in developing the content and pedagogy of *Investigations*:

Authors

Joan Akers

Michael T. Battista

Douglas H. Clements

Karen Economopoulos

Marlene Kliman

Jan Mokros

Megan Murray

Ricardo Nemirovsky

Andee Rubin

Susan Jo Russell

Cornelia Tierney

Contributing Authors

Mary Berle-Carman

Rebecca B. Corwin

Rebeka Eston

Claryce Evans

Anne Goodrow

Cliff Konold

Chris Mainhart

Sue McMillen

Jerrie Moffet

Tracy Noble

Kim O'Neil

Mark Ogonowski

Julie Sarama

Amy Shulman Weinberg

Margie Singer

Virginia Woolley

Tracey Wright

Contents

U N I T   6

Number Games and Crayon Puzzles

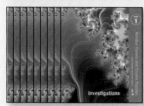

Investigations

CURRICULUM

Overview of Program Components

FOR TEACHERS

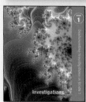

The **Curriculum Units** are the teaching guides. (See far right.)

Implementing Investigations in Grade 1 offers suggestions for implementing the curriculum. It also contains a comprehensive index.

The **Differentiation and Intervention Guide** offers additional activities for each Investigation to support the range of learners.

Investigations for the Interactive Whiteboard provides whole-class instructional support to enhance each session.

The **Resource Masters and Transparencies CD** contains all reproducible materials that support instruction. The **Shapes CD** provides an environment in which students investigate a variety of geometric ideas.

FOR STUDENTS

The **Student Activity Book** contains the consumable student pages (Recording Sheets, Homework, Practice, and so on).

The **Student Math Handbook** contains Math Words and Ideas pages and Games directions.

The *Investigations* Curriculum

Investigations in Number, Data, and Space® is a K–5 mathematics curriculum designed to engage students in making sense of mathematical ideas. Six major goals guided the development of the *Investigations in Number, Data, and Space®* curriculum. The curriculum is designed to:

- Support students to make sense of mathematics and learn that they can be mathematical thinkers

- Focus on computational fluency with whole numbers as a major goal of the elementary grades

- Provide substantive work in important areas of mathematics—rational numbers, geometry, measurement, data, and early algebra—and connections among them

- Emphasize reasoning about mathematical ideas

- Communicate mathematics content and pedagogy to teachers

- Engage the range of learners in understanding mathematics

Underlying these goals are three guiding principles that are touchstones for the *Investigations* team as we approach both students and teachers as agents of their own learning:

1. *Students have mathematical ideas.* Students come to school with ideas about numbers, shapes, measurements, patterns, and data. If given the opportunity to learn in an environment that stresses making sense of mathematics, students build on the ideas they already have and learn about new mathematics they have never encountered. Students learn that they are capable of having mathematical ideas, applying what they know to new situations, and thinking and reasoning about unfamiliar problems.

2. *Teachers are engaged in ongoing learning* about mathematics content, pedagogy, and student learning. The curriculum provides material for professional development, to be used by teachers individually or in groups, that supports teachers' continued learning as they use the curriculum over several years. The *Investigations* curriculum materials are designed as much to be a dialogue with teachers as to be a core of content for students.

3. *Teachers collaborate with the students and curriculum materials* to create the curriculum as enacted in the classroom. The only way for a good curriculum to be used well is for teachers to be active participants in implementing it. Teachers use the curriculum to maintain a clear, focused, and coherent agenda for mathematics teaching. At the same time, they observe and listen carefully to students, try to understand how they are thinking, and make teaching decisions based on these observations.

Investigations is based on experience from research and practice, including field testing that involved documentation of thousands of hours in classrooms, observations of students, input from teachers, and analysis of student work. As a result, the curriculum addresses the learning needs of real students in a wide range of classrooms and communities. The investigations are carefully designed to invite all students into mathematics—girls and boys; members of diverse cultural, ethnic, and language groups; and students with a wide variety of strengths, needs, and interests.

Based on this extensive classroom testing, the curriculum takes seriously the time students need to develop a strong conceptual foundation and skills based on that foundation. Each curriculum unit focuses on an area of content in depth, providing time for students to develop and practice ideas across a variety of activities and contexts that build on each other. Daily guidelines for time spent on class sessions, Classroom Routines (K–3), and Ten-Minute Math (3–5) reflect the commitment to devoting adequate time to mathematics in each school day.

About This Curriculum Unit

This **Curriculum Unit** is one of nine teaching guides in Grade 1. The sixth unit in Grade 1 is *Number Games and Crayon Puzzles*.

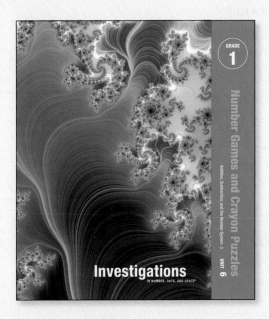

- The **Introduction and Overview** section organizes and presents the instructional materials, provides background information, and highlights important features specific to this unit.

- Each Curriculum Unit contains several **Investigations.** Each Investigation focuses on a set of related mathematical ideas.

- Investigations are divided into one-hour **Sessions,** or lessons.

- Sessions have a combination of these parts: **Activity, Discussion, Math Workshop, Assessment Activity,** and **Session Follow-Up.**

- Each session also has one or more **Classroom Routines** that are done outside of math time.

- At the back of the book is a collection of **Teacher Notes** and **Dialogue Boxes** that provide professional development related to the unit.

- Also included at the back of the book are the **Student Math Handbook** pages for this unit.

- The **Index** provides a way to look up important words or terms.

Overview

O F   T H I S   U N I T

Investigation	Session	Day	
INVESTIGATION 1 **Combinations of Ten** Students focus on combinations of 10 as they practice routines, play games, and solve story problems.	**1.1** Introducing 10	1	
	1.2 Three Towers	2	
	1.3 Make 10	3	
	1.4 Quick Images: Ten-Frames	4	
	1.5 Games About Missing Parts	5	
	1.6 Tens Go Fish	6	
	1.7 Combinations of 10	7	
INVESTIGATION 2 **Combinations of Numbers** Students develop strategies for combining numbers as they solve problems and play a variation of a familiar game.	**2.1** Revisiting How Many of Each? Problems	8	
	2.2 Crayon Puzzles About More	9	
	2.3 Dot Addition	10	
	2.4 More Crayon Puzzles	11	
	2.5 Assessment: Ten Crayons in All	12	
INVESTIGATION 3 **Addition and Subtraction** Students refine their understanding of the operations of addition and subtraction as they play games and solve story problems.	**3.1** Five-in-a-Row with Three Cards	13	
	3.2 Subtraction Games	14	
	3.3 Assessment: Counting On	15	
	3.4 Addition and Subtraction Story Problems	16	
	3.5 Solving Story Problems	17	
	3.6 Strategies for Adding	18	
	3.7 Strategies for Subtracting	19	
	3.8 End-of-Unit Assessment	20	

Each *Investigations* session has some combination of these five parts: **Activity, Discussion, Math Workshop, Assessment Activity,** and **Session Follow-Up.** These session parts are indicated in the chart below. Each session also has one **Classroom Routine** that is done outside of math time.

 Ⓦ Interactive Whiteboard

Activity	Discussion	Math Workshop	Assessment Activity	Session Follow-Up
Ⓦ●	●			●
Ⓦ●●				●
Ⓦ●		●		●
Ⓦ●		●		●
Ⓦ	●	●		●
Ⓦ●	●			●
Ⓦ	●	●		●
Ⓦ	Ⓦ			●
Ⓦ●	Ⓦ			●
Ⓦ●	Ⓦ			●
	Ⓦ	●		●
		●	Ⓦ	●
Ⓦ●●				●
Ⓦ●		●		●
Ⓦ		●	●	●
Ⓦ●				●
●	●●			●
	Ⓦ	●	●	●
	Ⓦ	●	●	●
			Ⓦ	●

Classroom Routines

Morning Meeting	Start With/ Get To	Quick Survey	Quick Images
	Ⓦ		
		Ⓦ	
	Ⓦ		
		Ⓦ	
	Ⓦ		
Ⓦ			
		Ⓦ	
	Ⓦ		
			Ⓦ
		Ⓦ	
	Ⓦ		
Ⓦ			
		Ⓦ	
	Ⓦ		
			Ⓦ
	Ⓦ		
	Ⓦ		
			Ⓦ
	Ⓦ		
Ⓦ			

Mathematics

Number Games and Crayon Puzzles is the sixth of 9 units in the Grade 1 sequence and the third of four units in the Grade 1 number strand. These units develop ideas about counting and quantity, the composition of numbers, and the operations of addition and subtraction.

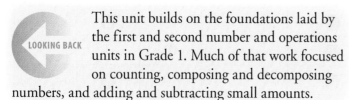

This unit builds on the foundations laid by the first and second number and operations units in Grade 1. Much of that work focused on counting, composing and decomposing numbers, and adding and subtracting small amounts.

At this point in the year, most students should be able to count accurately to over 50, both aloud and in writing; find more than two combinations of 2 addends that equal a number; make sense of story problems; and add and subtract small quantities accurately.

In this unit, students' work concentrates around three mathematical emphases:

1 Number Composition Composing numbers up to 20 with 2 or more addends

Math Focus Points

♦ Developing fluency with the 2-addend combinations of 10

♦ Finding relationships among different combinations of numbers up to 20

♦ Using $5 + 5$ to reason about other combinations of 10

♦ Finding as many 2-addend combinations of a number as possible

♦ Trying to prove that all the possible 2-addend combinations of a number have been found

Throughout Grade 1, students have experience breaking a number (a whole) into 2 or more parts, or combining 2 or more parts to form a whole. In the beginning of this unit, this work with composing and decomposing numbers is focused on an important landmark in our number system—10. In a variety of contexts, students work with combinations that equal 10 and explore relationships among those combinations.

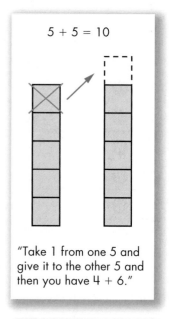

$5 + 5 = 10$

"Take 1 from one 5 and give it to the other 5 and then you have $4 + 6$."

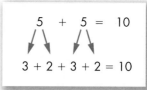

$$5 \quad + \quad 5 \quad = \quad 10$$
$$3 + 2 + 3 + 2 = 10$$

Most of this work is focused on the 2-addend combinations of 10 and helps students develop fluency with these combinations, which meets a benchmark at the end of Grade 1.

Being able to work with numbers in flexible ways lays crucial groundwork for future work in addition and subtraction. Thus, students also continue to develop an understanding of how *any* number (up to 20) can be composed and decomposed. One challenge for students continues to be finding *all* of the 2-addend combinations of a number and organizing their work in a way that shows they have found them all.

2 Whole Number Operations Making sense of and developing strategies to solve addition and subtraction problems with small numbers

Math Focus Points

◆ Solving related story problems

◆ Solving a problem in which the total and one part are known

◆ Adding 2 or more single-digit numbers

◆ Visualizing, retelling, and modeling the action in addition and subtraction (removal) situations

◆ Subtracting one number from another, with initial totals of up to 12

◆ Developing strategies for solving addition and subtraction story problems

◆ Solving addition and subtraction story problems

The addition and subtraction work of this unit continues to focus on making sense of the operations of addition and subtraction, practicing adding and subtracting single-digit numbers, and solving addition and subtraction story problems.

Although some students still *count all* to add 2 numbers, more and more *count on* with meaning at this point in the year, particularly in game contexts. (Some students count on to combine the results of a roll with a dot cube and number cube, but count all when solving a story problem about the same numbers.) A small but growing group use a combination or relationship they know (e.g., $6 + 4 = 10$ so $6 + 5 = 11$).

$$6 + 4 = 10$$
$$6 + 5 = 11$$
"I know that 6 + 4 is 10, so 6 + 5 is 11."

As for subtraction, most students *count all*. Some *count back, count up,* or use something they know (e.g., $14 - 5 = 14 - 4 - 1$).

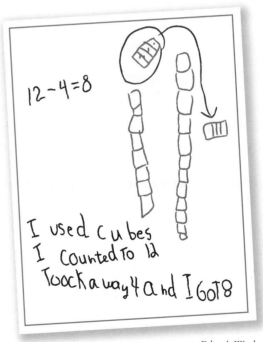

$12 - 4 = 8$

I used Cubes
I Counted To 12
Toock away 4 and I GoT 8

Edgar's Work

As in Unit 1 and Unit 3, the goal of the work with story problems is helping students develop strategies for visualizing the action of, and for solving, story problems. Toward that end, students' strategies are modeled with cubes, counters, or other tools, such as the number line, so that all students have the chance to make sense of the various methods being used to solve addition and subtraction story problems. There is a focus on naming and comparing different strategies (counting all, counting on/up, counting down/back, using known number combinations), as well as on using different tools (objects, pictures, fingers, the number line, the 100 chart).

Students use cubes to develop strategies to solve story problems.

3 Representing Mathematical Thinking Using manipulatives, drawings, tools, and notation to show strategies and solutions

Math Focus Points

◆ Using numbers and standard notation ($+$, $-$, $=$) to record

◆ Developing strategies for recording solutions to story problems

As in *How Many of Each?* (Unit 1) and *Solving Story Problems* (Unit 3), students see and use mathematical tools (cubes, fingers, number line, 100 chart) and representations (cubes, drawings, numbers, and notation) to model and solve problems and to clarify and communicate their thinking.

In particular, the focus is on helping children record the strategy used rather than a strategy that is easy to show. For example, some students fall back on drawing each individual item because they do not know how to show that they counted on. Therefore, teachers model different ways to record, using methods that come from students or ways that the class generates together (e.g., "Allie said she counted on her fingers. How could we show that up here on our chart paper?"). Efficiency is also a topic of discussion as students work on recording their work (e.g., "Do you need to show every single flower?").

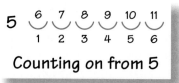

Counting on from 5

This Unit also focuses on

◆ Generating equivalent expressions for a number

◆ Developing strategies for counting and combining groups of dots

◆ Reasoning about more, less, and equal amounts

◆ Finding a solution that fits several clues

Classroom Routines focus on

◆ Developing strategies for counting accurately

◆ Using the calendar as a tool for keeping track of time

◆ Developing vocabulary to talk about time (morning, noon, midday, afternoon, etc.) and sequence (first, next, last, before, after, etc.)

◆ Collecting and recording data

◆ Estimating quantities up to about 30

◆ Adding or subtracting small amounts to/from a familiar number

◆ Investigating numbers that can (and cannot) be made into groups of two

◆ Counting, describing, and comparing data

◆ Making sense of a variety of representations of data

◆ Connecting written numbers and number names

◆ Using the 100 chart as a tool for counting

◆ Using the number line as a tool for counting

◆ Practicing the forward and backward counting sequences with numbers up to 100

◆ Developing and analyzing visual images for quantities

◆ Finding the total of two or more single-digit quantities

◆ Developing fluency with the addition combinations that make 10

◆ Using known combinations (i.e., combinations that make 10) to combine numbers

◆ Using standard notation ($+$, $-$, $=$) to write equations

◆ Collecting, counting, representing, describing, and comparing data

◆ Interpreting different representations of data including: pictures, bar graphs, tallies, and Venn Diagrams

LOOKING FORWARD The work with the 2-addend combinations of 10 lays the groundwork for achieving fluency with these combinations by the end of Grade 1. Unit 8, *Twos, Fives, and Tens,* focuses on these combinations, on numbers to 100, and on beginning to think about counting by groups. The addition and subtraction work is extended in second grade. In Grade 2, students solve a variety of kinds of addition and subtraction problems with larger numbers, explore a model for place value, and achieve fluency with the single-digit addition combinations. The focus of this work is on developing computational fluency—accuracy, efficiency, and flexibility—with the operations of addition and subtraction.

Assessment

IN THIS UNIT

ONGOING ASSESSMENT: Observing Students at Work

The following sessions provide **Ongoing Assessment: Observing Students at Work** opportunities:

- **Session 1.1, p. 30**
- **Session 1.2, p. 36**
- **Session 1.3, p. 42**
- **Session 1.5, p. 53**
- **Session 1.6, p. 58**
- **Session 1.7, p. 63**

- **Session 2.1, p. 71**
- **Session 2.2, p. 78**
- **Session 2.3, p. 84**
- **Session 2.4, p. 89**
- **Session 2.5, pp. 94–95**

- **Session 3.1, p. 105**
- **Session 3.2, pp. 109 and 110**
- **Session 3.4, p. 119**
- **Session 3.8, p. 136**

WRITING OPPORTUNITIES

The following sessions have **writing** opportunities for students to explain their mathematical thinking:

- **Session 1.4, p. 49**
  Student Activity Book, p. 7

- **Session 2.1, p. 71**
  Student Activity Book, p. 15

- **Session 2.2, p. 80**
  Student Activity Book, p. 20

PORTFOLIO OPPORTUNITIES

The following sessions have work appropriate for a **portfolio:**

- **Session 1.1, p. 29**
  Student Activity Book, p. 1

- **Session 2.1, p. 71**
  Student Activity Book, p. 15

- **Session 2.2, pp. 78 and 79**
  Student Activity Book, pp. 17 and 18

- **Session 2.5, p. 94**
  M39, Assessment: Ten Crayons in All

- **Session 3.4, p. 118**
  Student Activity Book, pp. 34–37

- **Session 3.8, p. 135**
  M55, End-of-Unit Assessment:
  Story Problems

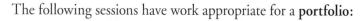

Assessing the Benchmarks

Observing students as they engage in conversation about their ideas is a primary means to assess their mathematical understanding. Consider all of your students' work, not just the written assessments. See the chart below for suggestions about key activities to observe.

See the **Differentiation and Intervention Guide** for quizzes that can be used after each Investigation.

Benchmarks in This Unit	Key Activities to Observe	Assessment
1. Find at least five 2-addend combinations of 10.	**Session 2.1:** Twelve Crayons in All	**Session 2.5 Assessment Activity:** Ten Crayons in All
2. Combine two small quantities by at least counting on.	**Sessions 3.3, 3.6, 3.7:** *Five-in-a-Row with Three Cards*	**Sessions 3.3, 3.6–3.7 Assessment Activity:** Assessment Checklist: *Counting On* 
3. Interpret (retell the action and sequence) and solve addition and subtraction story problems.	**Sessions 3.4–3.8** Story Problems	**Session 3.8 End-of-Unit Assessment:** Problem 1
4. Subtract one small quantity from another.	**Sessions 3.2–3.3, 3.6–3.7:** Subtraction Games	**Session 3.8 End-of-Unit Assessment:** Problem 2

✓ Checklist Available

Relating the Mathematical Emphases to the Benchmarks

Mathematical Emphases	Benchmarks
Number Composition Composing numbers up to 20 with two or more addends	1
Whole Number Operations Making sense of and developing strategies to solve addition and subtraction problems with small numbers	2, 3, 4

Algebra Connections

In this unit, your students will have opportunities to engage with ideas that lay a foundation for algebra. Six- and seven-year-old children can and do think algebraically. Part of the work of first grade is helping students learn to verbalize those thoughts, both as a way to engage with generalizations about number and operations and as a foundation for meaningful use of algebraic notation in the future.

At this point in the year, more students are likely to be using the ideas discussed in "Algebra Connections in This Unit," in *How Many of Each?* (Unit 1), and *Solving Story Problems* (Unit 3). Those students who have already been using these ideas may be getting better at verbalizing their thinking and demonstrating their ideas with cubes.

In this unit, students continue to learn about the number system. In particular, as they do this work, some students will begin to notice relationships involving addition and subtraction.

Consider the following vignette, in which Ms. Collins's class was discussing the following *Counters in a Cup* problem:

There are 9 counters altogether. 3 are showing outside the cup. How many are hidden inside?

Everyone agreed the answer was 6, but there were different strategies for figuring it out.

Jacinta: I started with 10 fingers. I put 1 down to make 9. Then I put down 3 fingers and I got 6.

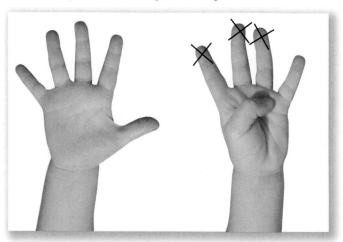

Marta: I put 3 in my head and counted up using my fingers until I got 9.

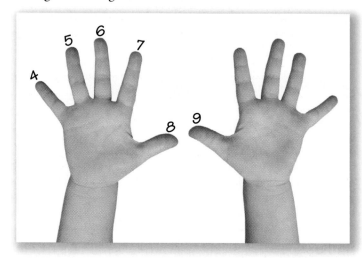

Teacher: Jacinta started with 9 and Marta started with 3, but they both got 6. Why is that? How come they both got the right answer?

Edgar: What difference does it make? The numbers are the same and they stay in the same order whether you go down or up.

Teacher: Can anyone write an equation for both Jacinta's and Marta's strategies?

The students suggested $9 - 3 = 6$ and $3 + 6 = 9$.

Carol: Hey, they're the same numbers but in a different order.

Relating Addition and Subtraction

When children first learn about addition and subtraction, they come to know them as distinct and unrelated actions. It often comes as a surprise to them to see that either operation can be used to solve the same problem. In this vignette, in order to find the number of counters inside the cup, Jacinta counted back from 9 to 3, and Marta counted up from 3 to 9. They both found the answer 6. When they represented these actions as equations, one involved subtraction, the other addition. Carol noticed that both equations used the same numbers but in different orders.

At this age, students should be encouraged to articulate their observations about such problems. As they repeatedly notice that the same problem can be solved by adding or subtracting, they will start to develop the expectation that any problem that can be solved by finding a missing addend can also be solved by subtracting, and vice versa, no matter the context or the numbers.

Students will also encounter the relationship between addition and subtraction as they work on related story problems. For example:

Vic and Libby were in charge of collecting pencils during cleanup time. Vic found 7 pencils and Libby found 3. How many pencils did they collect?

Libby and Vic put the 10 pencils in a pencil basket. Then Diego came by and took 3 of them for the kids at his table. How many pencils were left in the basket?

In the first problem, 7 and 3 are joined to make 10; in the second, 3 is removed from 10, leaving 7. Students are asked, Does the first problem help solve the second? If students say yes, how do they use the information from the first problem? Are they able to verbalize their thinking?

Although it will still be difficult for many students to articulate their thinking, some will have improved since the beginning of the year. You might hear students say "Seven and three come together to make 10. If 3 goes away, 7 is left and that's the answer."

As they get older, students will learn to express this same idea using variables: For any numbers, a, b, and c, if $a + b = c$, then $c - a = b$ and $c - b = a$.

For most adults, such notation (the use of variables, operations, and equal signs) is the chief identifying feature of algebra. The notation, however, expresses rules about how operations work that students can reason out for themselves. This reasoning—about how numbers can be put together and taken apart under different operations—not the notation, is the work of elementary students in algebra. *Investigations* students are encouraged to verbalize the generalizations they see about numbers and operations, and to explain and justify them using materials and tools, such as cubes.

The examples shown above illustrate the kind of "early algebraic reasoning," that is fully accessible to elementary-age students. This early algebra work involves students in reasoning, generalizing, representing, and communicating. It is not so much about finding an answer to a particular problem, but about describing a way to find answers to a whole class of problems. For example, the relationship between $7 + 3 = 10$ and $10 - 3 = 7$ is not only useful for solving $10 - 3$. Any subtraction problem has a related addition problem and vice versa.

Note: In the text for the sessions, you will find Algebra Notes that identify where these early algebra discussions are likely to arise. Some of the **Teacher Notes** and **Dialogue Boxes** further elaborate on the ideas and illustrate students' conversations about them.

Classroom Routines

Classroom Routines offer practice and review of key concepts for this grade level. These daily activities, to be done in ten minutes outside of math class, occur in a regular rotation every 4–5 days. Specific directions for the day's routine are provided in each session. For the full description and variations of each classroom routine see *Implementing Investigations in Grade 1*.

Morning Meeting

Students continue to use the calendar to keep track of time and events, collect and analyze data about the weather, and count the number of students in the class. Variations focus on solving problems based on the calendar.

Math Focus Points

◆ Developing strategies for counting accurately

◆ Using the calendar as a tool for keeping track of time

◆ Developing vocabulary to talk about time (morning, noon, midday, afternoon, etc.) and sequence (first, next, last, before, after, etc.)

◆ Collecting and recording data

◆ Counting, describing, and comparing data

◆ Estimating quantities up to about 30

◆ Adding or subtracting small amounts to/from a familiar number

◆ Investigating numbers that can (and cannot) be made into groups of two

Start With/Get To

Students practice counting forward and back with numbers to 60 on the 100 chart. They also count on the number line *from* a number between 0 and 50, *to* a number between 51 and 100 and then *from* a number between 51 and 100, *to* a number between 0 and 50.

Math Focus Points

◆ Connecting written numbers and number names

◆ Using the 100 chart as a tool for counting

◆ Using the number line as a tool for counting

◆ Practicing the forward and backward counting sequences with numbers up to 100

Quick Images

Students see and recreate one or more Ten Frames that focus on combinations that make 10. They determine the total number of dots and begin to think about equations that represent their thinking.

Math Focus Points

◆ Developing and analyzing visual images for quantities

◆ Finding the total of two or more single-digit quantities

◆ Developing fluency with the addition combinations that make 10

◆ Using known combinations (i.e., combinations that make 10) to combine numbers

◆ Using standard notation ($+$, $-$, $=$) to write equations

Quick Surveys

Students collect, organize, record, and discuss data about the class.

Math Focus Points

◆ Collecting, counting, representing, describing, and comparing data

◆ Interpreting different representations of data including: pictures, bar graphs, tallies and Venn diagrams

Practice and Review

Practice and review play a critical role in the *Investigations* program. The following components and features are available to provide regular reinforcement of key mathematical concepts and procedures.

Books	Features	In This Unit …
Curriculum Unit	**Classroom Routines** offer practice and review of key concepts for this grade level. These daily activities, to be done in ten minutes outside of math class, occur in a regular rotation every 4–5 days. Specific directions for the day's routine are provided in each session. For the full description and variations of each classroom routine see *Implementing Investigations in Grade 1*.	• **All sessions**
Student Activity Book	**Daily Practice** pages in the *Student Activity Book* provide one of three types of written practice: **reinforcement** of the content of the unit, **ongoing review,** or **enrichment** opportunities. Some Daily Practice pages will also have Ongoing Review items with multiple-choice problems similar to those on standardized tests.	• **All sessions**
	Homework pages in the *Student Activity Book* are an extension of the work done in class. At times they help students prepare for upcoming activities.	• **Session 1.4** • **Session 1.7** • **Session 2.2** • **Session 2.4** • **Session 3.2** • **Session 3.5**
Student Math Handbook	**Math Words and Ideas** in the *Student Math Handbook* are pages that summarize key words and ideas. Most Words and Ideas pages have at least one exercise.	• **Student Math Handbook, pp. 31, 33–42, 44–49**
	Games pages are found in a section of the *Student Math Handbook*.	• **Student Math Handbook, pp. G4, G5, G10, G11, G14, G15, G20, G23, G25**

Differentiation

Supporting the Range of Learners

The **Differentiation and Intervention Guide** provides Intervention, Extension, and Practice activities for use within each Investigation.

Sessions	1.1	1.2	1.3	1.4	1.5	1.6	1.7	2.1	2.2	2.3	2.4	2.5	3.1	3.2	3.3	3.4	3.6
Intervention	•		•	•	•	•	•	•	•				•	•		•	
Extension	•		•					•	•	•	•	•		•	•		•
ELL		•				•		•						•	•		

Intervention

Suggestions are made to support and engage students who are having difficulty with a particular idea, activity, or problem.

Extension

Suggestions are made to support and engage students who finish early or who may be ready for additional challenge.

English Language Learners (ELL)

In this unit, story problems are the main context through which students make sense of addition and subtraction and develop strategies to solve addition and subtraction problems.

English Language Learners may be challenged reading or understanding story problems depending on their facility with English. One way to assist English Language Learners develop an understanding of story problems is by providing multiple modalities of presentation, stressing the visual with pictures, manipulatives, or acting out the story problem.

For example, Investigation 1, Session 3 includes the following story: *Lyle and Isabel were in charge of collecting pencils during clean up time. Lyle found 7 pencils and Isabel found 3. (How many pencils did they collect?)* As you read the problem aloud, show 7 pencils in one hand and 3 pencils in another hand. Then bring the pencils together to show that the problem involves combining groups.

Another option is to have one student be Lyle and another student be Isabel. Read the first two sentences out loud and have the children act them out, using actual pencils.

English Language Learners will benefit, along with all students, from the modeling of their strategies with cubes, counters, number lines, etc. As strategies are named and compared in this unit, (counting all, counting on/up, counting down/back, using known number combinations), check for understanding by demonstrating or restating a students' strategy and asking other students (including English Language Learners) to name the strategy used. Since the Math Words and Ideas pages in the *Student Math Handbook* can be a particularly useful reference for English Language Learners, remind them to use these pages to look up or review the names of the addition and subtraction strategies used in this unit.

Working with the Range of Learners: Classroom Cases is a set of episodes written by teachers that focuses on meeting the needs of the range of learners in the classroom. In the first section, *Setting up the Mathematical Community,* teachers write about how they create a supportive and productive learning environment in their classrooms. In the next section, *Accommodations for Learning,* teachers focus on specific modifications they make to meet the needs of some of their learners. In the last section, *Language and Representation,* teachers share how they help students use representations and develop language to investigate and express mathematical ideas. The questions at the end of each case provide a starting point for your own reflection or for discussion with colleagues. See *Implementing Investigations in Grade 1* for this set of episodes.

Mathematical Emphases

Number Composition Composing numbers up to 10
with two addends

Math Focus Points

◆ Developing fluency with and generating the 2-addend
combinations of 10

◆ Finding relationships among different combinations of
numbers up to 10

◆ Using $5 + 5$ to reason about other combinations of 10

Whole Number Operations Making sense of and
developing strategies to solve addition and subtraction
problems with small numbers

Math Focus Points

◆ Solving related story problems

◆ Solving a problem in which the total and one part are known

Representing Mathematical Thinking Using
manipulatives, drawings, tools, and notation
to show strategies and solutions

Math Focus Points

◆ Using numbers and standard notation $(+, -, =)$ to record

This Investigation also focuses on

◆ Generating equivalent expressions for a number
◆ Developing strategies for counting and combining groups of dots

Combinations of Ten

SESSION 1.1 p. 26	Student Activity Book	Student Math Handbook	Professional Development: Read Ahead of Time	
Introducing 10 Students revisit *Quick Images,* using equations to describe different arrangements of 10 dots. Then they revisit Today's Number, generating expressions that equal 10.	1–2	48–49	• **Mathematics in This Unit,** p. 10 • **Teacher Note:** Using Notation, p. 139; About the Equal Sign, p. 141 • **Dialogue Box:** Pictures and Equations, p. 171; Today's Number: 10, p. 173	
SESSION 1.2 p. 33				
Three Towers Students revisit *Three Towers,* a game that involves using cubes of 2 colors to build 3 towers, each 10 cubes high. The session ends with the class solving several story problems about 10.	3–4	44–45, 48–49; G25	• **Algebra Connections in This Unit,** p. 16	
SESSION 1.3 p. 39				
Make 10 *Make 10,* a game that involves finding pairs of numbers that total 10, is introduced and included in a Math Workshop that focuses on combinations of 10. At the end of the session, the class solves more related problems about 10.	1, 5	44–45, 48–49; G15, G25		

Classroom Routines See page 18 for an overview.

Morning Meeting

- **Calendar** If necessary, prepare a new monthly calendar without any dates posted.

Start With/Get To

- **Baskets and pocket 100 chart** (from Unit 3)
- **Start With/Get To Cards, Sets A–C** (from Unit 3) Make copies of M6–M10 and cut apart the cards if necessary.

Quick Survey

- **Chart** Prepare a 2-column table titled "Do you have a pet?" on chart paper. Label the columns "Yes" and "No" respectively.
- **Chart** Prepare a 2-column table titled "Which do you like better, red or blue?" Label the columns "Red" and "Blue" respectively.
- **Chart** Prepare a horizontal table titled "Are you wearing the color green?," with the heading "Yes" or "No" written at the left of each row.

Materials to Gather	Materials to Prepare
• **Chart paper** (optional) • **Counters** (as needed) • **Connecting cubes** (12 per student)	• **T44,** *Quick Images:* **Pictures of 10** 🖨 Cut apart the images. Store them in an envelope or in the plastic sleeve of the Resources Binder. • **M1–M2, Family Letter** Make copies. (1 per student)
• **Connecting cubes** (60 in two colors; per pair) • **Dot cubes** (1 per pair) • **Number cubes** (1 per pair) • **Crayons** (in same 2 colors as connecting cubes; per pair) • **Cubes or counters** (12 per student or pair) • **Chart paper** (optional)	• **M4,** *Three Towers of 10* **Recording Sheet** Make copies. (as needed in this session; 1 per student for use in subsequent sessions) • **M5,** *Three Towers of 10* Make copies. (as needed)
• **Connecting cubes or counters** (as needed) • **Chart paper** (optional) • **Materials for** *Three Towers* See Session 1.2.	• **M13–M16, Primary Number Cards** If the cards from Unit 1 or Unit 3 need to be replaced, make copies on cardstock and laminate if available. Cut apart the cards. (1 deck per pair without wild cards; from Unit 1) • **M17,** *Make 10* Make copies. (as needed)

🖨 Overhead Transparency

Combinations of Ten,
continued

	Student Activity Book	Student Math Handbook	Professional Development: Read Ahead of Time
SESSION 1.4 p. 45			
Quick Images: Ten-Frames Class begins with *Quick Images* that show dots arranged in ten-frames. Math Workshop continues to focus on combinations of 10, and the session ends with more related problems about 10.	1, 6–7	48–49; G15, G25	
SESSION 1.5 p. 50			
Games About Missing Parts Students play *Counters in a Cup* and *How Many Am I Hiding?*, two games that involve finding a missing part. The session ends with a discussion about strategies for playing the new variation of these games.	9–11	48–49; G4, G14	
SESSION 1.6 p. 55			
Tens Go Fish Students learn, play, and discuss *Tens Go Fish,* a game that involves making combinations of 10 with two addends.	12	48–49; G23	
SESSION 1.7 p. 61			
Combinations of 10 Class begins with *Quick Images* of ten-frames. Math Workshop and class discussion focus on the 2-addend combinations of 10.	13–14	48–49; G4, G14, G15, G23	• **Teacher Note:** Strategies for Learning the Addition Combinations, p. 143

Materials to Gather	Materials to Prepare
• **Pennies or counters** (10 per student) • **Materials for *Three Towers*** See Session 1.2. • **Chart paper** (optional) • **Cubes or counters** (as needed) • **Materials for *Make 10*** See Session 1.3.	• **M18, Ten-Frame Cards** Make 4 copies per deck on cardstock. Cut apart the cards. (as needed; optional) • **T45, Ten-Frame Cards** 🖨 Cut apart the ten-frame cards. Store them in an envelope or in the plastic sleeve of the Resources Binder. (1 image per class plus extras for variation) • **M19, Blank Ten-Frames** Make copies for use during this Investigation. Cut apart the ten-frames. (several ten-frames per student) • **Homework materials** Each student will need a copy of *Make 10* (M17) and a deck of Primary Number Cards (M13–M16). Sets of Primary Number Cards were sent home in Unit 1. Make copies as needed.
• **Paper cups** (1 per pair) • **Color tiles in 2 colors** (5 of each color per student or pair) • **Connecting cubes in 2 colors** (5 of each color per student or pair)	• **M20, *Counters in a Cup* Recording Sheet** Make copies. (as needed in this session; 1 per student for use in Session 1.7) • **M21, *Counters in a Cup*** Make copies. (as needed) • **M22, *How Many Am I Hiding?* Recording Sheet** Make copies. (as needed) • **M23, *How Many Am I Hiding?*** Make copies. (as needed)
• **Chart paper** (optional) • **Primary Number Cards** (from Session 1.3) • **Card holders** (optional) • **Cubes or counters** • **T3–T6, Primary Number Cards** (optional) 🖨	• **M24, *Tens Go Fish*** Make copies. (as needed)
• **T45, Ten-Frame Cards** 🖨 • **Materials for *Tens Go Fish*** See Session 1.6. • **Materials for *Counters in a Cup* and *How Many Am I Hiding?*** See Session 1.5. • **Materials for *Make 10*** See Session 1.3. • **Chart paper** • **Pennies or counters**	

🖨 Overhead Transparency

Introducing 10

Math Focus Points

◆ Developing strategies for counting and combining groups of dots

◆ Generating equivalent expressions for a number

◆ Using numbers and standard notation (+, −, =) to record

Vocabulary

equation
equal sign

Today's Plan		Materials
❶ ACTIVITY *Quick Images: Pictures of 10*	20 MIN CLASS	• T44 • Chart paper (optional); counters
❷ ACTIVITY Today's Number: 10	30 MIN CLASS INDIVIDUALS	• *Student Activity Book*, p. 1 • Connecting cubes
❸ DISCUSSION Today's Number: 10	10 MIN CLASS	• Chart paper (optional)
❹ SESSION FOLLOW-UP Daily Practice		• *Student Activity Book*, p. 2 • *Student Math Handbook*, pp. 48–49 • M1–M2, Family Letter*

*See *Materials to Prepare*, p. 23.

Classroom Routines

Start With/Get To: Forward or Backward? Choose both the *start with* and *get to* numbers from a basket holding the numbers 1 to 60. Ask students to find and mark both numbers on the 100 chart. Decide as a class if you will be counting forward or backward (up or down). Have students take turns saying one number as they count their way around the circle from the *start with* to the *get to* number.

ACTIVITY

1 Quick Images: Pictures of 10

20 MIN   CLASS

To begin this Investigation, do several *Quick Images* that focus on different arrangements of 10 dots. As usual, students will need counters and/or paper and pencils. Begin by displaying the transparency of image A from *Quick Images: Pictures of 10* (T44), checking to make sure that all students can see the image clearly. Proceed through the routine as follows:

- Flash the image for about 5 seconds and then cover it. ❶

- Give students time to build or draw what they saw.

- Flash the image for another 5 seconds and then cover it.

- Allow time for students to revise or finish their first idea.

- Show the image a final time. This time leave it visible so that students can check their work and make any revisions.

Encourage students to describe and discuss what helped them remember the image.

- What helped you remember what the image looked like?

- What helped you make your copy?

Draw one or several sketches of image A on the board or on chart paper. After each student gives an explanation, record the ideas by circling the dots that the student saw grouped together.

Discuss how you can use an equation to show this way of breaking the image into parts.

[Tamika] said she saw a group of four on one end, a group of four on the other end, and two in the middle. How does that help you think about the total number of dots? How could we write that as an **equation**?

Students will probably suggest $4 + 2 + 4 = 10$ and $4 + 4 + 2 = 10$.

Teaching Note

❶ **Adjusting the Time** If you show the image for too long, students will draw from the picture rather than from their image of it; if you show it too briefly, they will not have time to form a mental image. Observe students to decide whether you need to adjust the amount of time you show an image.

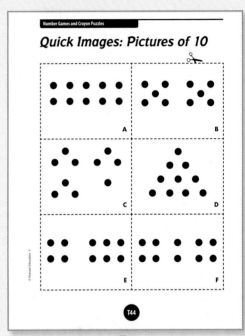

▲ Transparencies, T44

Professional Development

2 Dialogue Box: Pictures and Equations, p. 171

3 Teacher Note: Using Notation, p. 139

The Quick Images *routine in this session focuses on arrangements of 10 dots.*

Gather and record several ways of thinking about image A.**2** Note that while some students may be comfortable using equations to describe the way they thought about the images, others may need support.**3**

Repeat the activity with images B, C, and D. Or, if students find these images challenging, present E and F for more practice.

Your students are likely to notice that all the images in this set show 10 dots in all. If no one mentions it, ask students what they notice about the total number of dots in each image.

ACTIVITY

2 ## Today's Number: 10

30 MIN   CLASS   INDIVIDUALS

Provide each student or pair of students with 12 cubes. Ask students what they remember about the activity, Today's Number (from Unit 3). As needed, remind them that the task is to find many ways to make Today's Number.

Today we're going to continue working with the number 10. Today's Number is 10. I can show 10 with numbers [write "10"], with words [write "ten"] and with things [draw ||||| |||||, a picture of a train of 10 cubes, and refer students to the pictures of 10 from the beginning of the session].

Ask students what they know about the number 10. Use pictures, sketches, and numbers to record students' ideas. Also, ask students to help you write equations when appropriate.

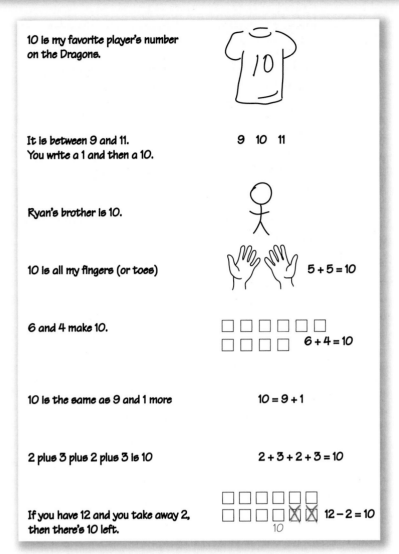

10 is my favorite player's number on the Dragons.

It is between 9 and 11.
You write a 1 and then a 10.

9   10   11

Ryan's brother is 10.

10 is all my fingers (or toes)

5 + 5 = 10

6 and 4 make 10.

6 + 4 = 10

10 is the same as 9 and 1 more

10 = 9 + 1

2 plus 3 plus 2 plus 3 is 10

2 + 3 + 2 + 3 = 10

If you have 12 and you take away 2, then there's 10 left.

12 − 2 = 10

10

Professional Development

Teacher Note: About the Equal Sign, p. 141

Name _____ Date _____

Number Games and Crayon Puzzles

Today's Number: 10
Today's Number is 10.

10
Ten

How many ways can you make Today's Number? Show the ways.

Session 1.1   Unit 6   1

© Pearson Education 1

▲ **Student Activity Book, p. 1** PORTFOLIO

[Chris] says that 3 and 7 make 10. Can someone show us with the cubes or with their fingers what that looks like? How could I record that on our chart about 10?

Some students may suggest drawing 3 cubes and 7 cubes; others might suggest 3 fingers and 7 fingers. Still others might suggest using addition notation: $3 + 7 = 10$ or $10 = 3 + 7$. If students have not suggested using the equal sign, introduce it yourself.

Take a few more suggestions of ways to make 10, reminding students that they can use more than two numbers and subtraction to make 10. If necessary, ask a volunteer to demonstrate each and record them on your chart.

Students should then work on their own to find ways to make 10, and record them on *Student Activity Book* page 1. Encourage all students to try to use numbers and equations to record their work.

ONGOING ASSESSMENT: Observing Students at Work

Students find many ways to compose and decompose the number 10. They are also thinking about how to use standard notation to record their work.

- **How are students coming up with combinations that make 10?** Do they work randomly? Use cubes or their fingers? Use number combinations they know? Are students using more than 2 addends? Subtraction?

- **How are students recording and annotating their work?** Are they using equations correctly?

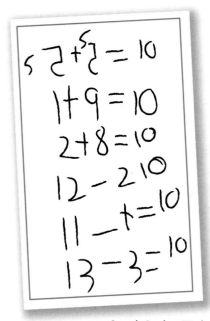

Sample Student Work

Sample Student Work

DIFFERENTIATION: Supporting the Range of Learners

Intervention Some students may benefit from using cubes to model the problem. These students may need help figuring out how to use an equation to describe what they did with cubes or pictures.

Extension Ask students who find several 2-addend combinations of 10 to find ways to make 10 that use more than two addends and/or subtraction.⑤

DISCUSSION

③ Today's Number: 10

10 MIN   CLASS

Math Focus Points for Discussion

◆ Generating equivalent expressions for a number

◆ Using standard notation (+, −, =) to record

Call the class together and ask students to share different ways they found to make 10. Record their combinations on chart paper or on the board.⑥

Students might say:

"I found 5 and 3 and 2 makes 10. I just know that 5 and 5 is 10. So I made one of the 5s into 3 plus 2. 5 plus 3 plus 2 is the same as 5 plus 5. They both make 10."

How could I use equations to record [Jacinta's] idea?

Record both equations and ask students to compare them. Model the relationship between the 2 equations with cubes, and add an illustration of that to your chart as well.⑦

▲ **Student Activity Book, p. 2**

In this discussion, students are encouraged to share strategies for making combinations of 10.

[Jacinta] said that she used a combination of 10 that she knew to find another combination. Did anybody else use a strategy like [Jacinta's]?

As time permits, ask several more students to share. Encourage them to check their *Student Activity Book* pages for ways to make 10 that are different from the ones already shared, but note that it will be challenging for students to decide and agree upon whether 2 + 3 + 5 is the same as or different from 5 + 3 + 2 (or another expression that lists the same numbers in a different order).

Students are expected to be fluent with the 2-addend combinations of 10 by the end of Grade 1. Explain to students that they will be thinking a lot about 10 and combinations that make 10 over the next week or so, and over the course of the rest of the year.

Students should save *Student Activity Book* page 1, as they will have the opportunity to continue to add to it in upcoming sessions.

SESSION FOLLOW-UP

Daily Practice

Daily Practice: For ongoing review, have students complete *Student Activity Book* page 2.

Student Math Handbook: Students and families may use *Student Math Handbook* pages 48–49 for reference and review. See pages 189–195 in the back of this unit.

Family Letter: Send home copies of the Family Letter (M1–M2).

Three Towers

Math Focus Points

◆ Developing fluency with the 2-addend combinations of 10

◆ Finding relationships among different combinations of numbers up to 10

◆ Solving related story problems

◆ Using numbers and standard notation (+ and =) to record

Vocabulary

story problem
more
fewer

Today's Plan		Materials
ACTIVITY ❶ **Introducing** *Three Towers*	15 MIN CLASS	• M4*; M5* • Connecting cubes; dot cube and number cube; crayons in same colors as connecting cubes
ACTIVITY ❷ **Playing** *Three Towers*	30 MIN PAIRS	• *Student Activity Book*, p. 3 • M4 • Connecting cubes; dot cubes; number cubes; crayons in same colors as connecting cubes
ACTIVITY ❸ **Stories About 10**	15 MIN CLASS	• Cubes or counters; chart paper (optional)
SESSION FOLLOW-UP ❹ **Daily Practice**		• *Student Activity Book*, p. 4 • *Student Math Handbook*, pp. 44–45, 48–49; G25

*See *Materials to Prepare*, p. 23.

Classroom Routines

Quick Survey: Have a pet? On chart paper, create a vertical 2-column table, titled "Do you have a pet?", with the column headings "Yes" and "No" written at the top of each column. Use tally marks to record students' responses and then count them as a class by fives and ones. After counting the responses, have a short discussion about the results of the survey.

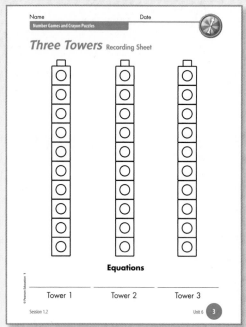

▲ **Student Activity Book, p. 3;**
Resource Masters, M4

15 MIN   CLASS

ACTIVITY

1 Introducing *Three Towers*

Students played *Three Towers* in Unit 1, *How Many of Each?* In this version, pairs work together to build 3 towers of 10 connecting cubes each. Players each choose one color of cubes. They take turns rolling a dot cube and a number cube. Then they form towers by snapping together connecting cubes in their chosen colors for the total number rolled. Players continue taking turns until they have 3 complete towers of 10, and then work together to record their work.

Reintroduce *Three Towers* by playing a demonstration game with a volunteer. You will need about 60 connecting cubes in 2 colors, a dot cube, a number cube, and a copy of *Three Towers of 10* Recording Sheet (M4).

- Player 1 rolls the dot cube and number cube, finds the total, and assembles that many connecting cubes of one color. If there are fewer than 10 cubes, the player makes one tower. If there are more than 10 cubes, the player makes a tower of 10 and begins a second tower with the leftover cubes.

- Player 2 rolls the cubes, finds the total, and assembles that many connecting cubes of another color. The player adds those cubes to the unfinished tower of 10, if there is one, and then starts a new tower with any remaining cubes.

- Players continue taking turns until they have built three complete towers of 10. (They do not need to roll an exact number to finish the game; extra cubes are set aside.)

- Players work together to show the number of connecting cubes of each color in each tower, and write an equation to match it on *Student Activity Book* page 3.

Demonstrate how to record on *Student Activity Book* page 3 by coloring each square of the first tower the appropriate color (or label each cube with letters that stand for the colors of the cubes). Then ask students to help you write an equation that matches it.

The last step is to write an equation that shows how many cubes of each color are in each tower. Let's look at the first tower. How many blue cubes are in this tower? [6] How many yellow? [4] How could we write an equation that describes our tower? [$6 + 4 = 10$ or $4 + 6 = 10$]

Player 1 rolls both cubes and assembles a connecting cube tower with that many cubes.

Player 2 rolls both cubes, completes the tower started by Player 1, and begins a new tower with the leftover connecting cubes.

The student records an equation.

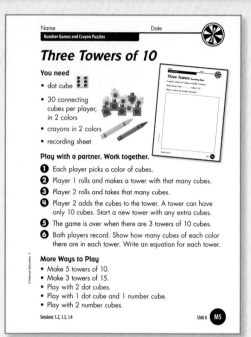

▲ **Resource Masters, M5**

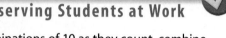

ACTIVITY

②Playing *Three Towers*

30 MIN | PAIRS

Pairs play *Three Towers* as you demonstrated.

ONGOING ASSESSMENT: Observing Students at Work

Students explore different combinations of 10 as they count, combine, and use addition notation to record.

- **How are students finding the total rolled?** Are more students successfully using a counting on strategy?

- **How do students determine when a tower is complete?** Do they keep recounting from 1? Count on from the last total? Match their tower to the towers pictured on *Student Activity Book* page 3? Use number combinations they know?

- **How do students figure out and record the total number of each color in each tower?** How accurately are they using addition notation?

Circulate as pairs play and clarify the directions as necessary. Use this time to ask questions about the numbers rolled and the totals found.

How many are in your tower so far? How many more do you need?

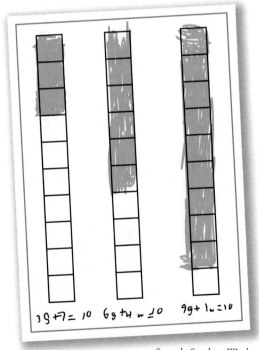

Sample Student Work

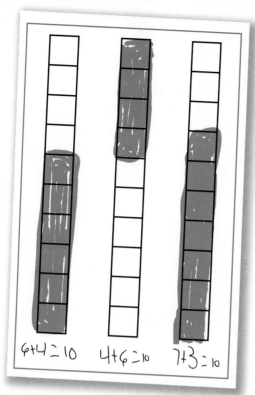

Sample Student Work

Story Problem Routine

1. Tell students a number story. Encourage them to visualize the action in the story.
2. Ask several students to retell the story. (Or, several students can each tell one part of the story. And occasionally, you might have each student retell the story to a partner.)
3. After each retelling of the story, ask whether the end result in each case will be more or less than the amount you started with.
4. Ask students to share strategies for solving the problem, including modeling the problem with cubes or counters.
5. Model methods of recording on chart paper or on the board.

Algebra Note

❶ **Commutative Property** These stories focus on the commutative property of addition (see **Algebra Connections in This Unit**, p. 16, in Unit 1, *How Many of Each?*). Students have already had some discussions about changing the order of addends. If they are ready to think further about this, you can ask, William said if we know $4 + 6 = 10$, then we know $6 + 4 = 10$. Would that *always* work? If you switch the order of 2 numbers does the total stay the same?

ACTIVITY

3 Stories About 10

15 MIN   CLASS

Give each student or pair a set of 12 cubes or counters. Then tell 2 related story problems about 10.

One day we had grapes for our snack. Allie had 4 red grapes. Edgar had 6 green grapes. How many grapes did they have altogether?

As previously established, ask students to retell the story, to think about whether there will be more or fewer grapes at the end of the story, and to share strategies for solving it. Record strategies on the board or chart paper as usual, including equations that model the problem situation.

Then tell another, related story.

Vic and Stacy were sitting at a table. Vic had 6 red grapes and Stacy had 4 green grapes. How many grapes did they have altogether?

Follow the same process but also encourage students to think about whether the first problem they solved can help them think about or solve the second.❶

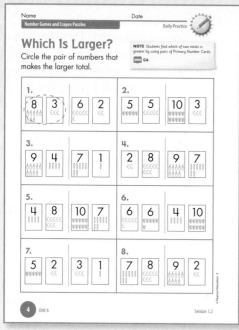

▲ Student Activity Book, p. 4

During this conversation, listen for evidence that some students are beginning to reason that it does not matter which group you count first. Use cubes or counters to model what those children are saying.

Students might say:

"Well in one, there's a pile of 4 and a pile of 6. In the other, there's a pile of 6 and a pile of 4. Either way there's still 10 grapes. It doesn't matter which you count first."

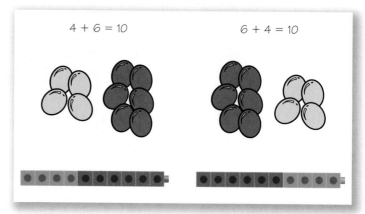

DIFFERENTIATION: Supporting the Range of Learners

ELL Story problems may continue to pose special challenges for English Language Learners, who may encounter a great deal of unfamiliar vocabulary in the stories. Take advantage of story problems to help English Language Learners develop their vocabulary. In the case of this story, bring in actual red and green grapes to show as you read the story. If that is not possible, cut out pictures of red and green grapes from a supermarket flyer, for example.

SESSION FOLLOW-UP

Daily Practice

 Daily Practice: For ongoing review, have students complete *Student Activity Book* page 4.

 Student Math Handbook: Students and families may use *Student Math Handbook* pages 44–45, 48–49 and G25 for reference and review. See pages 189–195 in the back of this unit.

Make 10

Math Focus Points

◆ Finding relationships among different combinations of numbers up to 10

◆ Developing fluency with the 2-addend combinations of 10

◆ Using numbers and standard notation (+ and =) to record

◆ Solving related story problems

Vocabulary

combine
plus sign

Today's Plan		Materials
ACTIVITY **❶ Introducing *Make 10***	15 MIN CLASS	• M13–M16*; M17* • Connecting cubes

MATH WORKSHOP **❷ Combinations of 10**
 ② Ⓐ *Make 10*
 ② Ⓑ *Three Towers*
 ② Ⓒ Today's Number: 10
	30 MIN	Ⓐ • M13–M16*
		   • Connecting cubes
		 Ⓑ • Materials from Session 1.2, p. 33
		   Use M4* in place of *Student Activity Book* p. 3
		 Ⓒ • *Student Activity Book*, p. 1 (from Session 1.1)
		   • Connecting cubes

ACTIVITY **❸ More Stories About 10**	15 MIN CLASS	• Cubes or counters; chart paper (optional)
SESSION FOLLOW-UP **❹ Daily Practice**		• *Student Activity Book*, p. 5 • *Student Math Handbook*, pp. 44–45, 48–49; G15, G25

*See *Materials to Prepare*, p. 23.

Classroom Routines

Start With/Get To Forward or Backward? Choose both the *start with* and *get to* numbers from a basket holding the numbers 1 to 60 (M6–M9). Ask students to find and mark both numbers on the 100 chart. Decide as a class if you will be counting forward or backward (up or down). As a class, count from the *start with* number to the *get to* number.

Primary Number Cards (page 1 of 4)

0	0	0	0
1	1	1	1
2	2	2	2

Sessions 1.3, 1.4, 1.6, 1.7, 3.1, 3.3, 3.6, 3.7

Unit 6 M13

▲ **Resource Masters, M13–M16; T3–T6**

ACTIVITY

1 Introducing *Make 10*

15 MIN   CLASS

To introduce *Make 10*, play a demonstration game with a volunteer. Provide pairs of students with 10 cubes. Then deal out 20 Primary Number Cards (M13–M16) in 4 rows of 5, face up. Keep the leftover cards face down in a pile nearby.

Today we're going to learn a new game called *Make 10*. To begin, you need 4 rows of number cards, with 5 cards in each row. The cards should be facing up.

Involve students in the game.

The goal of this game is to find two cards that you can combine to make 10. I'll start. Does anyone see two cards I could put together to make 10?

If students need help thinking of possible combinations, scan the rows for a pair that totals 10 and point to one of the cards in the pair.

What if I want to use the 7? Is there a card I could put with the 7 to make 10?

Some students may use the pictures on the cards, which are arranged in 2 rows of 5. They count the empty spaces to figure out that 7 + 3 is 10. Others may use cubes or count up on their fingers. Model these strategies as they come up.

Remove the cards that make 10 from the layout and set them aside. Fill the 2 empty spaces with cards from the top of the deck.

Now my partner takes a turn.

Again, if the player does not readily find a combination of 10, offer hints as needed.

Let's say William wants to use the 9. Is there another card he could put together with the 9 to make 10?

Continue taking turns. Be sure to model 10 + 0 as one combination and to explain that both players should keep each combination of 10 in a separate pile.

The game is over when no more combinations of 10 can be made. Sometimes there will be several cards left, but occasionally players may be able to use them all.

At the end of each turn, each player uses addition notation to record the combination of 10 on a separate sheet of paper. Model using the plus sign for the class.

This teacher models how to record combinations of 10 using addition notation.

MATH WORKSHOP

30 MIN

② Combinations of 10

Students should begin with the new game, *Make 10*. After playing rounds one or two, they can continue playing *Make 10* and then choose between *Three Towers* or Today's Number.

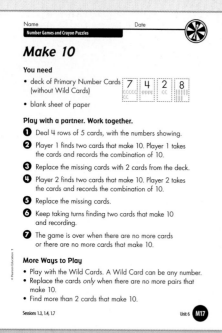

▲ Resource Masters, M17

2A *Make 10*

PAIRS

Students play in pairs as you demonstrated. Hand out *Make 10* (M17) as needed. If necessary, three students can play together or a student can play alone.

ONGOING ASSESSMENT: Observing Students at Work

Students are becoming familiar with the 2-addend combinations of 10, and are using addition notation to record.

- **What strategies do students use?** Do they seem to work randomly? Do they think about how many more they need to make 10? Do they look for particular combinations of 10?

- **How do students combine numbers?** Do they count from 1? Count on? Use number combinations they know?

- **How do students determine that the game is over?** Do they keep trying combinations of the cards that remain? Do they reason about the cards that remain? (*"5, 8, and 7 are left. I know we're done, because the 5 needs a 5, the 8 needs a 2, and the 7 needs a 3. And there's no 5, 2, or 3."*)

- **Do they record the combinations accurately?** Do they use addition notation correctly?

DIFFERENTIATION: Supporting the Range of Learners

Intervention Some students may benefit from playing another game with you in a small group. If students are randomly selecting combinations, show them how they can use cubes or the pictures on the cards to help them find a total of 10.

2B *Three Towers*

PAIRS

Have students play the game by following the procedure in Session 1.2, pages 34–37.

2C Today's Number: 10

INDIVIDUALS

Students revisit Today's Number: 10 from Session 1.1. They see whether they can find additional ways to make 10, and add these to *Student Activity Book* page 1.

For more details about this activity, see Session 1.1, pages 28–31.

ACTIVITY

3 More Stories About 10

15 MIN CLASS

Tell students two more related story problems about 10. For each, ask students to retell the story, to think about whether there will be more or fewer pencils at the end of the story, and to share strategies for solving it. Record strategies on the board or chart paper as usual, including equations that model the problem situation.

Lyle and Isabel were in charge of collecting pencils during clean up time. Lyle found 7 pencils and Isabel found 3. How many pencils did they collect?

Isabel and Lyle put the 10 pencils in a pencil basket. Then Diego came by and took 3 of them for the students at his table. How many pencils were left in the basket?

After posing the second problem, ask students to consider how the problem they have already solved might help them solve the new problem. Keep in mind that for many first graders, the second problem will seem like a new, unrelated problem. However, some students will connect $10 - 3 = ?$ (problem 2) to $7 + 3 = 10$ (problem 1). ❶

Students might say:

"We know that 7 and 3 make 10. That means you can break 10 into 7 and 3. So if you take away 3 from a 10, there's 7 left."

Algebra Note

❶ **Relating Addition and Subtraction** The relationship between addition and subtraction is an important idea. Students may not yet be able to verbalize how addition and subtraction are related. Comment on this relationship when it arises so that, over time, students will see it in a variety of contexts and forms. Say, for example, Edgar added to solve the problem and Talisa subtracted. They both got the same answers. Isn't that interesting? Students will revisit this idea throughout the elementary grades. (For more, see the **Algebra Connections in This Unit**, p. 16.)

Story Problem Routine

1. Tell students a number story. Encourage them to visualize the action in the story.
2. Ask several students to retell the story once they've heard it. (Or, several students can each tell one part of the story. And occasionally, you might have each student retell the story to a partner.)
3. After retelling each story, ask whether the end result in each case will be more or less than the amount you started with.
4. Ask students to share strategies for solving the problem, including modeling the problem with cubes or counters.
5. Model methods of recording on chart paper or the board.

As students explain their thinking, model it for the class.

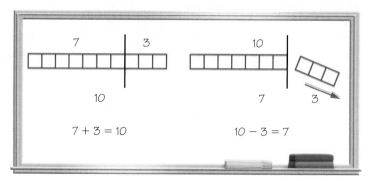

If there is time, try one more related problem.

What if there were 10 pencils in the pencil basket and Deshawn came by and took 7?

SESSION FOLLOW-UP

4 Daily Practice

 Daily Practice: For ongoing review, have students complete *Student Activity Book* page 5.

 Student Math Handbook: Students and families may use *Student Math Handbook* pages 44–45, 48–49, and G15, G25 for reference and review. See pages 189–195 in the back of this unit.

Quick Images: Ten-Frames

Math Focus Points

◆ Developing strategies for counting and combining groups of dots

◆ Using numbers and standard notation (+, −, =) to record

◆ Developing fluency with the 2-addend combinations of 10

◆ Solving related story problems

Vocabulary

ten-frame

Today's Plan		Materials
ACTIVITY **① Quick Images: Ten-Frames**	20 MIN CLASS	• T45 📄; M19* • Pennies or counters; chart paper (optional)
MATH WORKSHOP **② Combinations of 10** **2A** *Make 10* **2B** *Three Towers* **2C** *Today's Number: 10*	30 MIN	**2A** • Materials from Session 1.3, p. 39 • M18* (optional) **2B** • Materials from Session 1.2, p. 33 Use M4 in place of *Student Activity Book* p. 3. **2C** • *Student Activity Book*, p. 1 (from Session 1.1) • Connecting cubes
ACTIVITY **③ More Stories About 10**	10 MIN CLASS	• Chart paper (optional); cubes or counters
SESSION FOLLOW-UP **④ Daily Practice and Homework**		• *Student Activity Book*, pp. 6–7 • *Student Math Handbook*, pp. 48–49; G15, G25 • M13–M16*; M17*

*See *Materials to Prepare*, p. 25.

Classroom Routines

Quick Survey: Red or blue? On chart paper, create a vertical 2-column table titled "Which do you like better, red or blue?" with the column headings "Red" and "Blue" written at the top of each column. Use red and blue marks beneath the column headings to record the students' responses and then count them. After counting the responses, have a short discussion about the results of the survey.

Ten-Frame Cards

Number Games and Crayon Puzzles

T45

▲ Transparencies, T45

Math Note

❶ **Images of 10** This image is the same arrangement of dots as image A of *Quick Images: Pictures of 10* (T44, from Session 1.1), but placed in the ten-frame. Much as they did with that image, some students will see two rows of 5, others will see five groups of 2, and still others will see it differently (e.g., two groups of 4 and 2 more).

Professional Development

❷ **Dialogue Box:** Pictures and Equations, p. 171

ACTIVITY

❶ Quick Images: Ten-Frames

20 MIN   CLASS

Distribute a blank ten-frame (M19) and 10 pennies or counters to each student. Begin by displaying the transparency showing the image of the ten-frame with 10 dots. (T45)❶ Follow the regular *Quick Images* routine.

- Flash the image for about 5 seconds and then cover it.

- Give students time to build what they saw on their blank Ten-Frame.

- Flash the image for another 5 seconds and then cover it.

- Allow time for students to revise or finish their first idea.

- Show the image a final time. This time leave it visible so that students can check their work and make any revisions.

- Students describe and discuss what helped them remember the image.

Discuss the ways students remembered the image, being sure to establish that there are 10 squares in a ten-frame. Write equations that match the ways students see the image, while circling the various groups of dots.❷

Once students have established that there are 10 squares in a ten-frame, repeat the activity with several other images, such as the image with 8 dots. Use larger numbers, because that will encourage students to see, and allow you to record, the same image as both addition and subtraction.

Students might say:

"I saw 8 dots. There's 5 in one row, and 3 more."

"It's the same as the first one [10] but cover up 2 of the dots. 10 take away 2, that's 8."

In this discussion, students share ways they see an image of 8 dots on a ten-frame.

Some students will pay attention to the number of dots they see and others will think about the number of squares that have no dots,❸ or the number of squares in each row (knowledge about 5).

Teaching Note

❸ **Thinking About Subtraction** Some students are better able to see and pay attention to the squares with no dots if you place an **X** in them during the discussion.

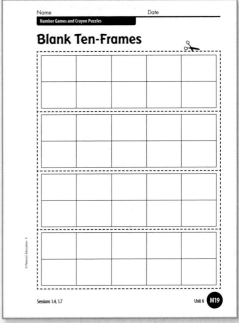

▲ Resource Masters, M19

MATH WORKSHOP

② Combinations of 10

⏲ **30 MIN**

Students continue to work on various activities about combinations that make 10.

②A *Make 10*

PAIRS

For complete details about this game, see Session 1.3, pages 40–42.

DIFFERENTIATION: Supporting the Range of Learners

(**Intervention**) Students who continue to struggle to find combinations that make 10 might benefit from playing with a deck of cards made from Ten-Frame Cards (M18). With these cards, students can often see more clearly how many dots need to be added to make 10.

(**Extension**) Students ready for more challenge can play with Wild Cards, or they can play with an added rule: do not fill in the empty spaces until all the possible combinations of 10 have been found.

<table>
</table>

Story Problem Routine

1. Tell students a number story. Encourage them to visualize the action in the story.
2. Ask several students to retell the story once they have heard it. (Or, several students can each tell one part of the story. And occasionally, you might have each student retell the story to a partner.)
3. After retelling each story, ask whether the end result in each case will be more or less than the amount you started with.
4. Ask students to share strategies for solving the problem, including modeling the problem with cubes or counters.
5. Model methods of recording on chart paper or the board.

2B *Three Towers*

PAIRS

For complete details about this game, see Session 1.2, pages 34–37.

2C *Today's Number: 10*

INDIVIDUALS

Students revisit Today's Number: 10 from Session 1.1. They see whether they can find additional ways to make 10 and add these to *Student Activity Book* page 1.

For details about this activity, see Session 1.1, pages 28–31.

ACTIVITY

10 MIN **CLASS**

3 More Stories About 10

Once again tell students two related story problems about 10. For each, ask students to retell the story, to think about whether there will be more or fewer objects at the end of the story, and to share strategies for solving it. Record strategies on the board or chart paper as usual, including equations that model the problem situation.

Out on the playground, there were children playing tag. I saw eight girls and two boys playing tag. How many children were there?

Ten children were playing tag on the playground. Seth and Paul decided to play on the swings instead. How many children were still playing tag?

After posing the second problem, ask students to consider how the problem they have already solved might help them solve the new problem. Do not expect all students to use the first problem to solve the second, but continue to ask students who do to explain and model their thinking for their classmates.

Students might say:

"If you put 8 and 2 together, that's 10. That's the first problem. The second one says there's 10 and 2 left. That leaves 8."

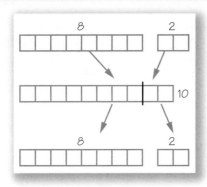

If there is time, try one more related problem:

What if 10 children were playing tag and 8 of them decided to play on the swings? How many children would still be playing tag?

SESSION FOLLOW-UP
Daily Practice and Homework

 Daily Practice: For reinforcement of this unit's content, have students complete *Student Activity Book* page 6.

 Homework: Have students play *Make 10* with someone at home. Students should already have a deck of Primary Number Cards (M13–M16) at home. They will need a copy of *Make 10* (M17). Tell students that the person with whom they play should help them complete and return *Student Activity Book* page 7.

 Student Math Handbook: Students and families may use *Student Math Handbook* pages 48–49 and G15, G25 for reference and review. See pages 189–195 in the back of this unit.

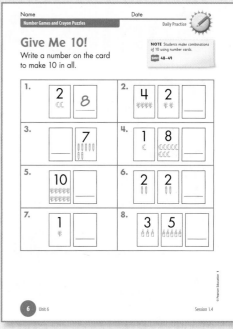

▲ **Student Activity Book, p. 6**

▲ **Student Activity Book, p. 7**

Games About Missing Parts

Math Focus Points

- Solving a problem in which the total and one part are known
- Finding relationships among different combinations of numbers up to 10
- Using numbers to record
- Using 5 + 5 to reason about other combinations of 10

Today's Plan		Materials
1 ACTIVITY **Introducing Games About Missing Parts**	15 MIN CLASS	• M20*; M21*; M22*; M23* • Color tiles in 2 colors; paper cup; connecting cubes in 2 colors
2 MATH WORKSHOP **Games About Missing Parts** **2A** *Counters in a Cup* **2B** *How Many Am I Hiding?*	30 MIN	**2A** • *Student Activity Book,* p. 9 • M20*; M21* • Paper cups; color tiles in 2 colors **2B** • *Student Activity Book,* p. 10 • M22*; M23* • Connecting cubes in 2 colors
3 DISCUSSION **Strategies for Games About Missing Parts**	15 MIN CLASS	• Color tiles in 2 colors; paper cup
4 SESSION FOLLOW-UP **Daily Practice**		• *Student Activity Book,* p. 11 • *Student Math Handbook,* pp. 48–49, G4, G14

*See *Materials to Prepare,* p. 25.

Classroom Routines

Start With/Get To Counting Forward Divide the Start With/Get To cards between two baskets labeled *start with* (cards 1–50) and *get to* (cards 51–100) (M10–M13). Choose a *start with* number from the first basket and a *get to* number from the second. Ask students to find and mark both numbers on the number line. As a class, count from the *start with* number to the *get to* number.

ACTIVITY

Introducing Games About Missing Parts

15 MIN **CLASS**

Counters in a Cup and *How Many Am I Hiding?* are games that involve finding the missing part. In this unit, the games are played with 10 counters or cubes—5 of one color and 5 of another color. In each game some counters or cubes are hidden from view. Students use what they know about the total (10) and the number visible to figure out how many are hidden.

Remind students that they have played these games earlier in the year. Explain that this time students will play with 10 counters, 5 each of two colors. ❶

It will be helpful if you remember that there are 5 of each color. You can use this information to help you figure out how many counters are hidden.

Reintroduce *Counters in a Cup* by playing a sample round with a volunteer. Show students a paper cup and 10 counters—5 of one color and 5 of another. Agree that there are 10 counters altogether and 5 of each color. Then, secretly hide one counter under the cup. Put the remaining counters outside the cup so all students can see them.

How many counters did I hide? Why do you think that [1] is hidden? How did you figure that out? Did anyone use the clue that there were 5 [blue] and 5 [red] counters?

Students may use various strategies to figure out how many are hidden, such as:

• Re-creating the situation with counters, counting on from 9 up to 10

• Counting back from 10 to 9

• Reasoning about groups of 5 (e.g., *"There were 5 red and 5 blue. Now there are 5 red and 4 blue, so there's 1 blue hidden."*)

Demonstrate recording the combination of 10 on *Counters in a Cup* Recording Sheet (M20). Explain that pairs will play this together, taking turns hiding the counters, but that both students will record. The game is over when all of the rows are filled. Have available copies of *Counters in a Cup* (M21) for students to remember the game rules.

Teaching Note

❶ **Color Tiles as Counters** In this variation of *Counters in a Cup*, students need counters of two colors. Color tiles work well for this variation.

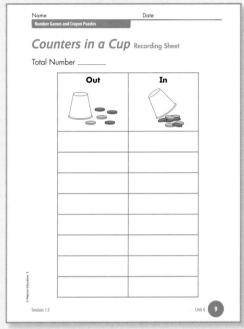

▲ **Student Activity Book, p. 9; Resource Masters, M20**

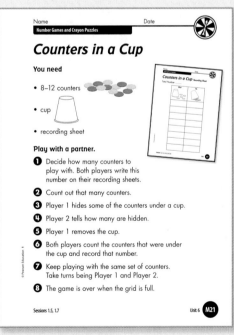

▲ **Resource Masters, M21**

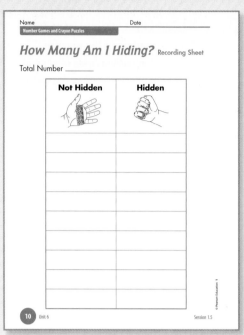

▲ **Student Activity Book, p. 10;
Resource Masters, M22**

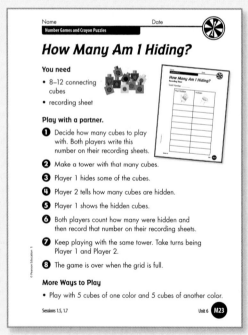

▲ **Resource Masters, M23**

*This student reasons about groups of 5 in order
to figure out that one blue counter is hidden.*

Reintroduce *How Many Am I Hiding?* by playing a sample round. Show students a tower of 10 cubes made up of 5 of one color and 5 of another color.

We all agree that there are 10 cubes, 5 [reds] and 5 [blues]. I'm going to break my tower into 2 parts, and I'm going to hide 1 part behind my back [break off 2 and hide them]. There are 8 showing.

How many cubes am I hiding? Why do you think that [2] are hidden? How did you figure that out?

Demonstrate recording the combination of 10 on *How Many Am I Hiding?* Recording Sheet (M22). Explain that pairs will play this together, taking turns hiding the cubes, but that both students will record. The game is over when all the rows are filled. Have available copies of *How Many Am I Hiding?* (M23) as needed.

MATH WORKSHOP

2 Games About Missing Parts

30 MIN

Partners should play both games. Students record on their own recording sheets. Have copies of the recording sheets available.

Encourage players to vary the number of counters or cubes they hide (including all or none if they do not try it on their own). However, they can occasionally hide the same number more than once.

2A Counters in a Cup

PAIRS

Have students play the game by following the procedure you demonstrated.

2B How Many Am I Hiding?

PAIRS

Have students play the game by following the procedure you demonstrated.

ONGOING ASSESSMENT: Observing Students at Work

Students are exploring how the two parts (number of counters or cubes showing and the number hidden) and a whole (total number of counters or cubes) are related.

- **How do students figure out how many counters or cubes are hidden?** Do they guess? Count the visible counters and then count on? Use knowledge of combinations of 10? Use a prior solution? (*"Last time, there were 3 outside the cup and 7 hidden. This time, there are 2 outside so there must be 8 hidden."*) Reason about groups of 5? (*"There are 5 blues and 2 reds showing. There are 5 reds altogether so there must be 3 reds hidden because 3 and 2 are 5."*)

- **How accurate and legible is students' written work?**

- **Do students understand that the amount showing and the amount hidden always equal the total number?**

DIFFERENTIATION: Supporting the Range of Learners

Intervention Some students may need their own cup and counters, or set of cubes, to directly model the problem.

DISCUSSION

3

15 MIN   CLASS

Strategies for Games About Missing Parts

Math Focus Points for Discussion

- Solving a problem in which the total and one part are known
- Using $5 + 5$ to reason about other combinations of 10

Pose a *Counters in a Cup* problem for the class to solve.

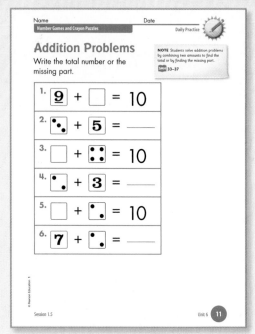

▲ **Student Activity Book, p. 11**

I have 10 counters altogether, 5 [blue] and 5[red]. Let's count them to be sure we agree. Now I'm going to hide some under my cup. [Hide 4.] Look at how many are showing. How many do you think I hid? Does anyone think there's a different number under my cup?

Ask students to share their strategies for figuring out how many counters were hidden. Strategies will likely include the following:

- Using fingers (e.g., *"I have 10 fingers and here are the 6 counters that are showing. So 4 are hidden because I have 4 fingers left."*)

- "Just knowing" that 6 and 4 are 10

- Counting up or on from 6 to 10

- Using what they know about 5 (e.g., *"There were 5 blues, now there's only 1. So you hid 4."*)

Once strategies have been shared, focus students' attention on this last one, reasoning about groups of 5 to figure out how many are hidden.

How did knowing that there were 5 [blue] and 5 [red] counters help you play this game?

Encourage students to explain their thinking.

Students might say:

 "There were 5 blues, but now there's only 1. 1 and 4 make 5, so 4 must be hidden."

Let's try another problem. See if this strategy helps you solve the problem.

Try another problem or two, encouraging students to use what they know about 5 to solve the problem.

SESSION FOLLOW-UP
④ Daily Practice

Daily Practice: For reinforcement of this unit's content, have students complete *Student Activity Book* page 11.

Student Math Handbook: Students and families may use *Student Math Handbook* pages 48–49 and G4, G14 for reference and review. See pages 189–195 in the back of this unit.

Tens Go Fish

Math Focus Points

- Developing fluency with and generating the 2-addend combinations of 10
- Finding relationships among different combinations of numbers up to 10
- Solving a problem in which the total and one part are known
- Using numbers and standard notation (+ and =) to record

Today's Plan			Materials
ACTIVITY **①Introducing** *Tens Go Fish*	🕐 20 MIN	👨‍👧‍👦 CLASS	• M24*; T3–T6 (optional)* 🖨 • Primary Number Cards; chart paper (optional)
ACTIVITY **②Playing** *Tens Go Fish*	🕐 25 MIN	👥 PAIRS	• Primary Number Cards (from Session 1.3); Ten-Frame Cards (from Session 1.4; optional); card holders (optional)*; cubes or counters
DISCUSSION **③Strategies for** *Tens Go Fish*	🕐 15 MIN	👨‍👧‍👦 CLASS	• Connecting cubes; chart paper (optional)
SESSION FOLLOW-UP **④Daily Practice**			• *Student Activity Book,* p. 12 • *Student Math Handbook,* pp. 48–49; G23

*See *Materials to Prepare,* p. 25.

Classroom Routines

Morning Meeting: Mixed Up Calendar Follow your daily *Morning Meeting* Routine. During Calendar, choose three date cards and change their position on the calendar so that they are out of order. Ask students to find the mistakes and to help you fix them.

Differentiation

❶ **English Language Learners** You might want to meet with English Language Learners ahead of time to preview the rules and object of this game, as well as demonstrate the meanings of words such as *pair, draw,* and *turn.* As you explain the rules, be sure to have a set of cards so you can demonstrate each of the rules and the directions of the game. If it is not possible to meet with English Language Learners beforehand, be sure to demonstrate the meaning of unfamiliar words as you introduce the game to the whole class.

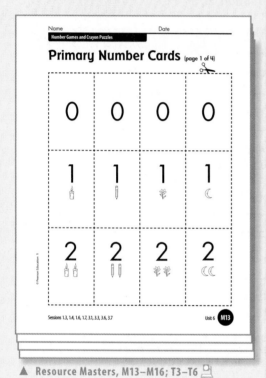

▲ Resource Masters, M13–M16; T3–T6

ACTIVITY

① Introducing *Tens Go Fish*

20 MIN   CLASS

Tens Go Fish is derived from the familiar card game, *Go Fish.* Display the following transparent Primary Number Cards (T3–T6) on the overhead, or draw them on the board or on chart paper:

We're going to learn the game *Tens Go Fish.* The goal is to find pairs of cards that add up to 10. Each player gets five cards to start. Let's say these are the cards in my hand: 4, 1, 5, 7, and 9. Can I make 10 with two of these cards?❶

Give students time to think about the problem and to share ideas.

I could make 10 with the 1 and the 9. That's my first pair.

Put the 1 and 9 cards down, as a pair, off to one side.

When the game starts, I look at my cards. If I have a pair that makes 10, I can put those down and then pick two more cards.

Replace the cards you have put down with two more cards, [a 4 and a 2 for example.] Make sure that you have no pairs of cards in your hand that make 10.

Let's say I picked a 4 and a 2. Now my cards are 4, 2, 4, 5, and 7. Do any two of these cards make 10?

After students agree that there is not a pair that makes 10, explain:

I don't have two cards that make 10. So, when it's my turn, I can ask the other player for a card that I need to make 10. Suppose I wanted to use my 2 to make 10. What card would I need to add to the 2 to make 10?

Ask students how they figured out what number to ask for.

Imagine I am playing with [Carol]. I might ask, "[Carol], do you have an 8?" If [Carol] has an 8, she gives it to me. I put down the 8 and 2. If [Carol] does not have an 8, she says, "Go fish" and I take a card from the top of the deck.

Each time I pick a new card, I check to see whether I can make 10 with that card and a card that's already in my hand. If I can, I put the pair down. If I can't, my turn is over. If I run out of cards, I can pick two new cards from the deck.

Play a demonstration game with a volunteer. Explain that you will be showing students your cards so that they can learn how to play. When students play in pairs, however, they will not show their cards to their partners. As you play, involve students in your turn.

Put each pair of cards that makes 10 in a separate pile. Explain that this is so the cards do not get mixed up because at the end of the game, players will record all the combinations of 10 that they found. Model this for students.

Continue until most students understand how to play. Explain that the game is over when there are no more cards in the desk. On blank paper, model how to record the combinations of 10 using an equation. If 10 and 0 cards did not come up in one hand during the demonstration game, find these cards and be sure students recognize that they make a pair.

In the game Tens Go Fish, *players look for pairs of cards that make combinations of 10.*

▲ **Resource Masters, M24**

ACTIVITY

② Playing *Tens Go Fish*

25 MIN   PAIRS

Students play *Tens Go Fish* in pairs as you demonstrated. Have available copies of *Tens Go Fish* (M24) as needed.

ONGOING ASSESSMENT: Observing Students at Work

Students continue to work on the 2-addend combinations of 10. They are also solving a problem about a missing part each time they ask for a particular card (*e.g., "I have a 7, I need 10, what do I need to ask for?"*)

- **How easily are students able to find pairs of cards that equal 10?**

- **How do students decide which card to ask for?** Do they seem to ask for cards at random? Do they use counting strategies? Knowledge of combinations of 10?

- **Are students able to keep track of the cards that other players have asked for?** Do they use this to reason about what cards the other player has?

DIFFERENTIATION: Supporting the Range of Learners

Intervention Some students may benefit from playing with you in a small group before playing independently with a partner. Using a tower of 10 cubes to model the situation can help some students figure out what to ask for.

Here are 10 cubes. You said you want to use the 7. How can this tower help us figure out what you should ask for?

Other students fare better playing with ten-frame cards, as the cards help students see more clearly how many more they need to get to 10. Provide these students with decks of ten-frame cards cut from Ten-Frame Cards (M18).

DISCUSSION

③ Strategies for *Tens Go Fish*

15 MIN   CLASS

Math Focus Points for Discussion

◆ Solving a problem in which the total and one part are known

◆ Developing fluency with combinations of 10

Give 10 connecting cubes to each student or pair. Then pose several story problems based on the game *Tens Go Fish*.

Imagine that [Richard] and [Felipe] are playing *Tens Go Fish*. [Richard] wants to use his 3. What card should he ask [Felipe] for?

Ask students to share strategies for figuring this out. Then have students use cubes to model their strategies for classmates.

Students might say:

"I used 10 cubes. He has 3. So he needs to ask for a 7."

"He has 3. If you count on, it's 7 to get to 10."

"The question was 3 plus what equals 10. I just know that 3 + 7 is 10."

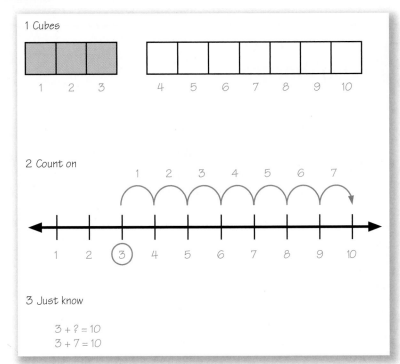

Record the strategies as usual, asking students to help you use equations to model the use of known addition combinations.

Algebra Note

 Students have discussed the fact that when you change the order of addends, the total stays the same. Note whether they call upon that idea when asked how the first problem relates to the second.

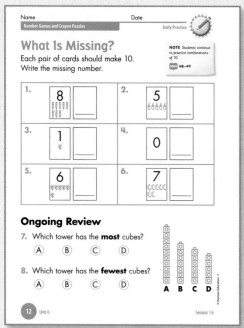

▲ Student Activity Book, p. 12

What did we know at the beginning of this problem? (*Richard had a 3.*) What else did we know? What total was Richard trying to make? (*10*) What didn't we know? What were we trying to figure out? *(how many to add to 3 to make 10)* So we knew that Richard had a 3. And we knew that he was trying to figure out what number when added to 3 makes 10.

$$3 + ? = 10 \quad \text{or} \quad 3 + \boxed{7} = 10 \quad \text{or} \quad 3 + \underline{7} = 10 \quad \text{or} \quad 3 + 7 = 10$$

Follow the same process with a second, related story.

Now imagine that Talisa and Libby are playing. Libby wants to use a 7. What should she ask Talisa for?

Continue to ask students whether they see a relationship between such related problems, and note whether any use the first to solve the second. If you model the notation above as 1 way to record, students might be more likely to see the relationship between the 2 problems and among the 3 numbers in the problems once both equations are filled in.

$$3 + \boxed{7} = 10$$
$$7 + \boxed{3} = 10$$

SESSION FOLLOW-UP

4 Daily Practice

Daily Practice: For reinforcement of this unit's content, have students complete *Student Activity Book* page 12.

Student Math Handbook: Students and families may use *Student Math Handbook* pages 48–49 and G23 for reference and review. See pages 189–195 in the back of this unit.

Combinations of 10

Math Focus Points

◆ Finding relationships among different combinations of numbers up to 10

◆ Developing fluency with the 2-addend combinations of 10

◆ Solving a problem in which the total and one part are known

◆ Generating 2-addend combinations of 10

Vocabulary

combination

Today's Plan		Materials
ACTIVITY **1 *Quick Images: Ten-Frames***	20 MIN CLASS	• T45, 🖨 (from Session 1.4); M19, (from Session 1.4) • Pennies or counters
MATH WORKSHOP **2 Games About Combinations of 10** **2A *Tens Go Fish*** **2B *Counters in a Cup*** **2C *How Many Am I Hiding?*** **2D *Make 10***	25 MIN	**2A** • Materials from Session 1.6, p. 55 **2B** • Materials from Session 1.5, p. 50 Use M20 in place of *Student Activity Book*, p. 9. **2C** • Materials from Session 1.5, p. 50 Use M22 in place of *Student Activity Book*, p. 10. **2D** • Materials from Session 1.3, p. 39
DISCUSSION **3 Combinations of 10**	15 MIN CLASS	• Chart paper
SESSION FOLLOW-UP **4 Daily Practice and Homework**		• *Student Activity Book*, pp. 13–14 • *Student Math Handbook*, pp. 48–49; G4, G14, G15, G23

Classroom Routines

Quick Survey: Wearing green? On chart paper, create a *horizontal* table, titled "Are you wearing the color green?", with the headings "Yes" and "No" written at the left of each row. Use tally marks to record students' responses and then count them by fives and ones. After counting the responses, have a short discussion about the results of the survey.

ACTIVITY

① *Quick Images:* Ten-Frames

Distribute copies of Blank Ten-Frames and 10 pennies or counters to each student. Do several rounds of *Quick Images* using transparencies of Ten-Frame Cards (T45). Follow the regular routine.

- Flash the image for about 5 seconds and then cover it.

- Give students time to build what they saw on their blank ten-frame.

- Flash the image for another 5 seconds and then cover it.

- Allow time for students to revise or finish their first idea.

- Show the image a final time. This time leave it visible so that students can check their work and make any revisions.

- Students describe and discuss what helped them remember the image. Write equations that match the ways students see the image while circling the various groups of dots.

As students briefly view a Quick Images Ten-Frame, *they practice visualizing quantities.*

As you discuss the images, explore how the work students have been doing relates to the ten-frame images. For example, use the image for 6 and relate it to *Tens Go Fish*.

We all agree that there are 6 dots in this image. Think about the games you've been playing. Imagine that we're playing *Tens Go Fish* and I have a 6. What do I need to ask for? How do you know? How could this image help you?

Students might say:

 "Well, there's 6 dots and there's 10 squares. So you'd need 4 more dots, 1 for each empty square."

 "The squares with dots plus the squares without dots is 10."

Because ten-frames are made of two rows of 5, you can also connect the games *How Many Am I Hiding?* and *Counters in a Cup* to these *Quick Images,* as the variations played in this unit use 5 as an important landmark number.

MATH WORKSHOP

 25 MIN

Games About Combinations of 10

Students choose any of the combinations of 10 games that they have learned during this Investigation.

2A *Tens Go Fish*

 PAIRS

For complete details about this game, see Session 1.6, pages 56–58.

ONGOING ASSESSMENT: Observing Students at Work

See Session 1.6, page 58.

DIFFERENTIATION: Supporting the Range of Learners

Intervention See Session 1.6, page 58.

Extension For more challenge, students can play in small groups of 3 or 4 players. With more players, it is more difficult to remember the cards other players have asked for.

2B and **2C** *Counters in a Cup and How Many Am I Hiding?*

PAIRS

For complete details about these games, see Session 1.5, pages 51–53.

DIFFERENTIATION: Supporting the Range of Learners

Extension Challenge students to figure out whether their finished game sheets show all of the possible combinations of 10.

2D *Make 10*

PAIRS

For complete details about this game, see Session 1.3, pages 40–42.

DIFFERENTIATION: Supporting the Range of Learners

Extension Students who are ready for more challenge can play with a variation of the original rules: find any combination of cards that make 10. In this version, 5 + 3 + 2 would be an acceptable combination of 10.

Some students may be ready to play Make 10 *by finding combinations of 3 or more cards that make 10.*

15 MIN   CLASS

DISCUSSION
③ Combinations of 10

Math Focus Points for Discussion

◆ Generating 2-addend combinations of 10

Students may need to refer to the various recording sheets from the 10-related games and activities in Investigation 1 as they work to generate a list of combinations of 10.

Begin the discussion by reminding students of the 10-related work they have done.

We've been doing a lot of work with the number 10. We've been thinking about how to make 10, how to break apart 10, and we've been working really hard on combinations of 2 numbers that make 10.

Explain to students that you would like to make a list of all of the ways to make 10 by adding 2 numbers together.

Record each combination on chart paper, recording "turnarounds" or "opposites" such as 8 + 2 and 2 + 8 next to each other.❶ Before recording each suggestion, ask students to check whether it is already listed. This can help students begin to notice relationships among solutions.

$$
\begin{array}{ll}
5 + 5 & \\
9 + 1 & 1 + 9 \\
8 + 2 & 2 + 8 \\
10 + 0 & \\
4 + 6 & 6 + 4
\end{array}
$$

Note that you will be assessing students' developing fluency with these 2-addend combinations of 10 at the end of this unit. Students are expected to be fluent with the combinations of 10 by the end of first grade.❷

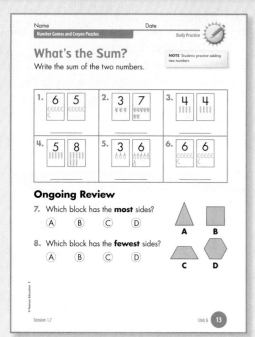

▲ Student Activity Book, p. 13

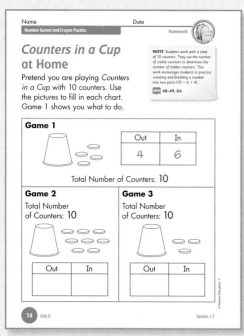

▲ Student Activity Book, p. 14

4 Daily Practice and Homework

 Daily Practice: For ongoing review, have students complete *Student Activity Book* page 13.

 Homework: Send home *Student Activity Book* page 14. Students complete the page to show how many counters are hidden, based on the total number and the number of counters they see.

 Student Math Handbook: Students and families may use *Student Math Handbook* pages 48–49 and G4, G14, G15, G23 for reference and review. See pages 189–195 in the back of this unit.

Mathematical Emphases

Number Composition Composing numbers up to 20 with 2-addends

Math Focus Points

◆ Finding relationships among different combinations of numbers up to 20

◆ Finding as many 2-addend combinations of a number as possible

◆ Trying to prove that all the possible 2-addend combinations of a number have been found

Whole Number Operations Making sense of and developing strategies to solve addition and subtraction problems with small numbers

Math Focus Points

◆ Adding 2 or more single-digit numbers

Representing Mathematical Thinking Using manipulatives, drawings, tools, and notation to show strategies and solutions

Math Focus Points

◆ Using numbers and standard notation $(+, -, =)$ to record

This Investigation also focuses on

◆ Reasoning about more, less, and equal amounts
◆ Finding a solution that fits several clues

Combinations of Numbers

	Student Activity Book	Student Math Handbook	Professional Development: Read Ahead of Time	
SESSION 2.1 p. 70				
Revisiting How Many of Each? Problems Students revisit How Many of Each? problems, trying to find all the possible combinations of 12 red and blue crayons.	15–16	46–47	• **Teacher Note:** About How Many of Each? Problems in This Unit, p. 145 • **Dialogue Box:** Do We Have *All* of the Combinations?, p. 174	
SESSION 2.2 p. 76				
Crayon Puzzles About More Students are introduced to Crayon Puzzles, a variation of How Many of Each? problems. They solve and discuss puzzles that give a total number of red and blue crayons and a clue about how many of each color there are.	17–20	46–47	• **Teacher Note:** About Crayon Puzzles, p. 147 • **Dialogue Box:** Introducing Crayon Puzzles, p. 176	
SESSION 2.3 p. 81				
Dot Addition Students learn, play, and discuss a new variation of the game *Dot Addition*.	21	G5	• **Teacher Note:** Building on Number Combinations You Know, p. 149	
SESSION 2.4 p. 88				
More Crayon Puzzles Students spend most of the session in a Math Workshop focused on combinations of numbers. The session ends with a discussion about a Crayon Puzzle.	17–18, 22–25	46–47, 48–49; G5	• **Dialogue Box:** I Think There's Only 3 Ways, p. 177	
SESSION 2.5 p. 93				
Assessment: Ten Crayons in All Students solve a How Many of Each? problem about 10 crayons, and then continue with activities focused on combinations of numbers.	22–23, 27	46–47, 48–49; G5	• **Teacher Note:** Assessment: Ten Crayons in All, p. 151	

Ten-Minute Math See page 18 for an overview.

Morning Meeting	Quick Images
• **Calendar** Mark class events and holidays on the monthly calendar.	• **T45, Ten-Frame Cards** . Gather transparencies of ten-frame cards prepared in Investigation 1.

Start With/Get To	Quick Survey
• Baskets and pocket 100 chart • **M6–M12, Start With/Get To Cards** (from Investigation 1)	• Venn Diagram with 2 circles. Label the inside of one circle "I have a brother" and the second circle "I have a sister." See page 81.

Materials to Gather	Materials to Prepare
• **Red and blue connecting cubes** (as needed) • **Red and blue crayons** (as needed) • **Chart paper** • **Red and blue markers** (1 of each color)	• **M25–M26, Family Letter** Make copies. (1 per student)
• **Red and blue connecting cubes or color tiles** (10 of each color per student or pair)	
• **Cubes or counters** (as needed; optional) • **Chart paper** (optional)	• **M27, *Dot Addition* Cards** Make copies. (1 deck per pair) • **M28, *Dot Addition* Gameboard A** Make copies for use during this Investigation. (3 per pair per game) • **M29, *Dot Addition*** Make copies. (as needed) • **M30, *Dot Addition* Blank Gameboard** Make copies. (as needed; optional)
• **Materials for *Dot Addition*** See Session 2.3. • **Red and blue connecting cubes or color tiles** (15 of each color per student or pair) • **Green connecting cubes** (as needed; optional) • **Chart paper** (optional)	• **M31–M36, Challenging Crayon Puzzles** Make copies for use during this Investigation. (as needed; optional) • **M37–M38, *Dot Addition* Gameboards B and C** Make copies. (as needed; optional)
• **Counters and other tools** • **Materials for *Dot Addition*** See Session 2.3. • **M31–M36, Challenging Crayon Puzzles** (as needed) • **Cubes or tiles** (optional)	• **M37–M38 and M40–M41, *Dot Addition* Gameboards B through E** Make copies. (as needed; optional) • **M39, Assessment: Ten Crayons in All** Make copies. (1 per student)

 Overhead Transparency

Revisiting How Many of Each? Problems

Math Focus Points

◆ Finding relationships among different combinations of a number

◆ Finding as many 2-addend combinations of a number as possible

◆ Trying to prove that all the possible 2-addend combinations of a number have been found

Today's Plan		Materials
① ACTIVITY **Twelve Crayons in All**	40 MIN CLASS INDIVIDUALS	• *Student Activity Book,* p. 15 • Red and blue connecting cubes; red and blue crayons
② DISCUSSION **Discussing Combinations of 12**	20 MIN CLASS	• Chart paper; red and blue markers
③ SESSION FOLLOW-UP **Daily Practice**		• *Student Activity Book,* p. 16 • *Student Math Handbook,* pp. 46–47 • M25–M26, Family Letter*

*See *Materials to Prepare,* p. 69.

Classroom Routines

Start With/Get To Counting Forward Choose the *start with* number from the first basket (cards 1–50) and the *get to* number from the second (cards 51–100). Ask students to find and mark both numbers on the number line. After counting aloud as a class, have students write the numbers from the *start with* number to the *get to* number.

ACTIVITY
Twelve Crayons in All

40 MIN   CLASS   INDIVIDUALS

Remind students of the How Many of Each? problems they solved earlier in the year, and ask what they remember about them. Then pose today's problem.

We are going to solve a How Many of Each? problem today. Imagine a crayon box that holds 12 crayons. There are 12 crayons in my box. If the crayons are red and blue, what combinations of crayons could I have in my crayon box? How many reds? How many blues? Remember, I need 12 crayons in all.

Have one or two students model a possible combination, but keep the introduction short.

Just like the last few times we did these problems, your job is to try to find as many combinations of red and blue crayons as you can. Try to find all of the possible combinations. If you think you have found all of the combinations of 12 red and blue crayons, think about how you could convince someone that you have found all the ways. ❶

Remind students to show their work on *Student Activity Book* page 15 in a way that would help someone else understand what they did. Encourage them to try to use numbers and equations in their written work.

✓ ONGOING ASSESSMENT: Observing Students at Work

Students find many 2-addend combinations of a number. Trying to find *all* of the possible combinations and prove that they have them all encourages students to work more systematically and to find ways to organize and keep track of their work.

- **How do students model and solve the problem?**

- **How many combinations do students find?** How do students decide whether they have them all? How sure are they? ❷

- **How do students record their solutions?**

In preparation for the discussion at the end of this session, identify students who have strategies for finding many combinations and for recording their work. ❸ ❹

Math Note

❶ **All of the Combinations** Note that we do not expect all first graders to find every single solution and a way to justify that they have them all. But presenting students with this challenge often pushes all students further with this type of problem.

Algebra Note

❷ **Using "Opposites"** When students use one combination to find another (i.e., using "opposites," or changing one red into a blue), ask them to explain how they know they did not change the number of crayons. You might also ask if they can apply the same strategy to other combinations.

Professional Development

❸ **Teacher Note:** About How Many of Each? Problems in This Unit, p. 145

❹ **Dialogue Box:** Do We Have *All* of the Combinations?, p. 174

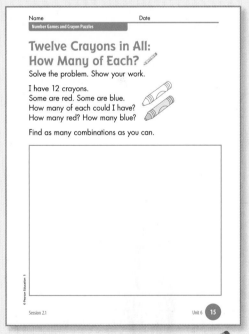

▲ **Student Activity Book, p. 15** PORTFOLIO WRITING

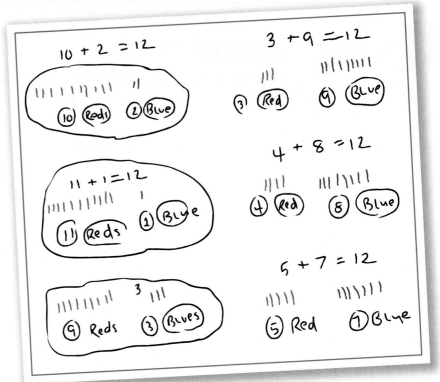

Sample Student Work

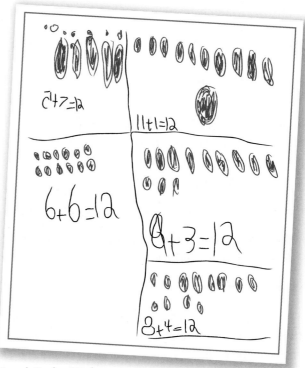

Sample Student Work

DIFFERENTIATION: Supporting the Range of Learners

Intervention Ask students who have found only a few solutions to try to find more. Encourage others to develop a system for keeping track of the combinations they have found and to compare their solutions with those of other students.

Extension If students are sure they have found all the combinations, challenge them to find a way to prove it. They can also solve a related problem: What if there were red, blue, and green crayons? How many of each could I have?

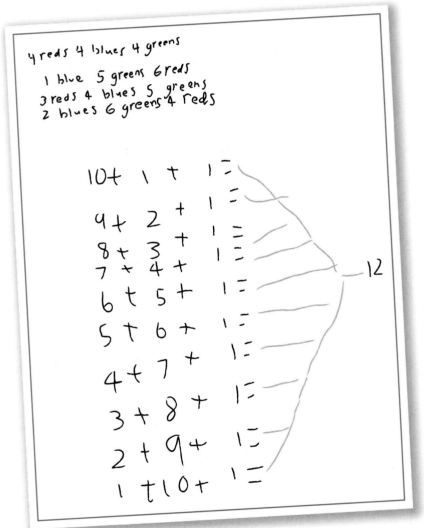

Sample Student Work

Differentiation

⑤ **English Language Learners** English Language Learners may be reluctant to share their strategies if they do not yet have a comfortable level of oral fluency in English. To encourage their participation in class discussions, begin by asking simple and clear yes/no questions about their strategies and solutions. Help English Language Learners participate by making note of their strategies and solutions as they are working and then including these where appropriate. For example, "So far we have two ways to make 12 crayons in all— 1 red crayon plus 11 blue crayons and 2 red crayons and 10 blue crayons. Isabel started with 3 red crayons. Isabel, can you write that on our chart? Can you write how many blue crayons you need for 12 crayons in all?"

Teaching Note

⑥ **What about 12 + 0?** Given the context of this problem "some are red and some are blue," 12 + 0 would not be a possibility. Some classrooms, however, decided together that it would be acceptable to have 0 of one color, thus including 12 + 0 and 0 + 12 as possibilities.

DISCUSSION
2 Discussing Combinations of 12

20 MIN   CLASS

Math Focus Points for Discussion

◆ Finding as many 2-addend combinations of a number as possible

◆ Trying to prove that all the possible 2-addend combinations of a number have been found

Make a class chart titled "Twelve Crayons in All" for recording students' combinations.

Ask students who you observed working more systematically—using ordered lists or thinking about "opposites"—to share their strategies for finding many solutions and for organizing and recording their work.

Then ask students to share solutions, and use one of the suggested ideas to record them.⑤

[Seth] suggested putting the number of reds or blues first every time. Let's start with the smallest number of red crayons. Who thinks they have a combination with the smallest number of red crayons in it? Who thinks they have the combination that should come next?

Twelve Crayons in All		
R		B
1	+	11 = 12
2	+	10 = 12
3	+	9 = 12
4	+	8 = 12
5	+	7 = 12
6	+	6 = 12
7	+	5 = 12
8	+	4 = 12
9	+	3 = 12
10	+	2 = 12
11	+	1 = 12

Ordered list

Twelve Crayons in All

1 + 11= 12   11 + 1 = 12

2 + 10 = 12   10 + 2 = 12

3 + 9 = 12   9 + 3 = 12

4 + 8 = 12   8 + 4 = 12

5 + 7 = 12   7 + 5 = 12

6 + 6 = 12   6 + 6 = 12

Opposites

Record all of the combinations that students found.⑥

We found a lot of different ways! Do you think we have found *all* of the ways to make 12 red and blue crayons? Why do you think so? Do you think there are any ways that are missing? Why do you think so?

Some students will be unsure, thinking that if you keep trying new numbers, you will find another combination. Others will be fairly sure that you have all of the ways, but will have a hard time explaining why they are sure. Encourage students to explain their thoughts, which are likely to include some variation on the following:

Students might say:

"We decided that you can't use 0 or 12 because you have to have some of each. And we have 1, 2, 3, . . . 11 red crayons (tracing down the red crayon column) and 1, 2, 3 . . . 11 blue crayons (tracing up the blue crayon column)."

"It goes from 1 red crayon all the way up to 11 red crayons. There's no numbers missing so there's no other ways (with red crayons). And the same is true for blue."

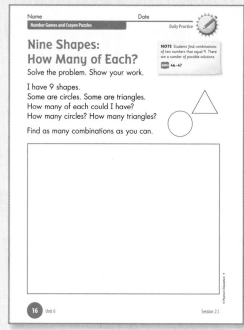

Student Activity Book page

▲ **Student Activity Book, p. 16**

SESSION FOLLOW-UP
3 Daily Practice

 Daily Practice: For ongoing review, have students complete *Student Activity Book* page 16.

 Student Math Handbook: Students and families may use *Student Math Handbook* pages 46–47 for reference and review. See pages 189–195 in the back of this unit.

 Family Letter: Send home copies of the Family Letter (M25–M26), which provides suggestions for activities to do at home.

Crayon Puzzles About More

Math Focus Points

◆ Finding relationships among different combinations of a number

◆ Reasoning about more, less, and equal amounts

◆ Finding a solution that fits several clues

Vocabulary

more

Today's Plan		Materials
ACTIVITY ❶ **Introducing Crayon Puzzles About More**	15 MIN · CLASS	• Red and blue connecting cubes
ACTIVITY ❷ **Solving a Crayon Puzzle About More**	30 MIN · INDIVIDUALS · PAIRS	• *Student Activity Book,* pp. 17–18 • Red and blue connecting cubes or color tiles
DISCUSSION ❸ **Crayon Puzzle 1**	15 MIN · CLASS	• *Student Activity Book,* p. 17 (completed work) • Red and blue connecting cubes
SESSION FOLLOW-UP ❹ **Daily Practice and Homework**		• *Student Activity Book,* pp. 19–20 • *Student Math Handbook,* pp. 46–47

Classroom Routines

Quick Images Ten Frames Show transparencies of two Ten Frame Cards (T45) that total 10 beginning with 7 and 3. Follow the basic *Quick Images* activity. Ask students to determine the total number of dots and to share their strategies. Repeat with the combinations 6 and 4 and then, 5 and 5.

15 MIN   CLASS

ACTIVITY

① Introducing Crayon Puzzles About More

Professional Development

❶ **Teacher Note:** About Crayon Puzzles, p. 147

❷ **Dialogue Box:** Introducing Crayon Puzzles, p. 176

Crayon Puzzles are a variation of the How Many of Each? problems that students have solved over the course of Grade 1. They add another piece of information, or rule, that students need to take into account. First-grade students differ widely in how readily they can solve these kinds of puzzles. ❶

Today we are going to solve a new kind of problem called Crayon Puzzles. Here's an example. I have 5 blue and red crayons. There are more blue crayons than there are red crayons. How many of each could I have?

As with story problems, encourage students to listen to and picture the problem as you read it, and to describe it in their own words.

Students will likely comment on the similarity of this problem to a How Many of Each? problem. Ask them to think about how it is *different*.

[Allie] said there's an extra rule for this problem. It says, *there are more blue crayons than red.*

To make sure that students understand the clue involving *more,* show students 5 cubes—4 reds and 1 blue. Ask which color there are *more* of, and then have students help you change it so that there are *more blue cubes.*

We need a combination of 5 crayons that has *more blue than red* crayons.

Ask one or two students to share a solution and to model it with red and blue cubes. ❷ Model ways to check solutions against the original clues. For example, you can make a tower of the blue cubes and a tower of the red cubes and compare the heights to check that there are *more* blue cubes than red cubes.

Does [Richard's] solution have 5 crayons total? Does it have more blue crayons than red crayons?

Discussions about whether the number of blue crayons is more than the number of red crayons offers an opportunity to revisit the > and < symbols, which were introduced to students in Unit 3.

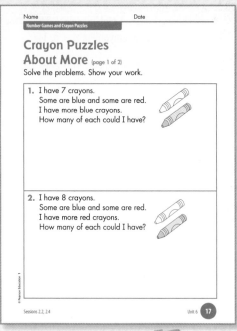

This teacher models one way to check solutions to Crayon Puzzles.

ACTIVITY

2 Solving a Crayon Puzzle About More

30 MIN · INDIVIDUALS · PAIRS

Introduce Crayon Puzzle 1 by reading it aloud.

I have 7 crayons. Some are blue and some are red. I have *more* blue crayons. How many of each could I have?

Together, discuss the known and unknown information for this puzzle. Explain what materials are available for solving the problem, and remind students to record their work on *Student Activity Book* page 17.

ONGOING ASSESSMENT: Observing Students at Work

Crayon Puzzles are more challenging than How Many of Each? problems because they contain another clue (the relative size of each set), which introduces an additional condition that students' answers must meet.

- **How do students solve the puzzle?** Do they generate combinations randomly until they find one that matches all the clues? Do they find a set that matches the total, and then adjust? Do they use knowledge of number combinations?

- **Do students look for more than 1 solution?** Do they treat each new solution as a separate problem? Do they find new solutions by changing something about a solution they already have?

- **How do they record their work?**

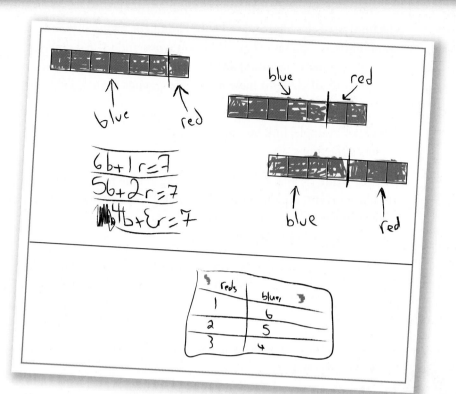

$$6b + 1r = 7$$
$$5b + 2r = 7$$
$$4b + 3r = 7$$

reds	blue
1	6
2	5
3	4

Sample Student Work

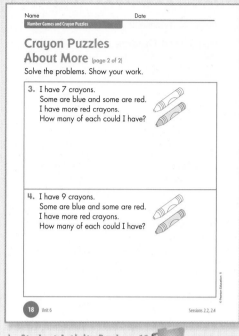

▲ Student Activity Book, p. 18

DIFFERENTIATION: Supporting the Range of Learners

Intervention Some students may benefit from working through the problem with you in a small group.

Extension Challenge students who finish quickly to think about whether they have found *all* of the possible answers that fit the clues. Students who have (and are confident that they have) found all the answers can solve the other puzzles on *Student Activity Book* pages 17 and 18.

DISCUSSION

3 **Crayon Puzzle 1**

15 MIN   CLASS

Math Focus Points for Discussion

◈ Reasoning about more, less, and equal amounts

◈ Finding a solution that fits several clues

Spend a few minutes discussing puzzle 1 on *Student Activity Book* page 17. Check each solution that students suggest against both of the clues.

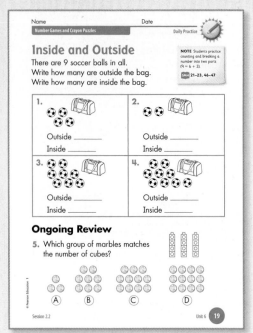

▲ Student Activity Book, p. 19

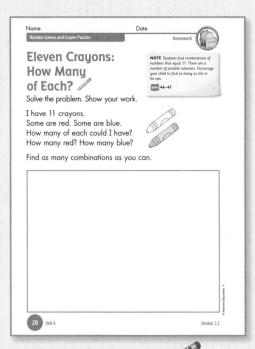

▲ Student Activity Book, p. 20

[Jacinta] used the blue and red cubes and kept trying different combinations. She says that [4] blue crayons and [3] red crayons work. Let's check [Jacinta's] answer. Does [Jacinta's] solution have 7 crayons in all? Does it have *more* blue crayons than red crayons?

As you discuss various strategies and solutions, try to tie them to each other. For example, link one student's work with cube towers to another student's equations.

[Bruce] wrote [5 + 2 = 7]. He wrote [5] in blue to show that those are blue crayons, and he wrote [2] in red. Does anyone see [Bruce's] answer in the cube towers that [Paula] made? How many blue cubes should there be? How many red?

At the end of the discussion, have students save *Student Activity Book* pages 17 and 18, as they will continue working on these pages in Session 2.4.

SESSION FOLLOW-UP

Daily Practice and Homework

Daily Practice: For ongoing review, have students complete *Student Activity Book* page 19.

Homework: Students solve a How Many of Each? problem and record their solution strategies on *Student Activity Book* page 20.

Student Math Handbook: Students and families may use *Student Math Handbook* pages 46–47 for reference and review. See pages 189–195 in the back of this unit.

Dot Addition

Math Focus Points

◆ Adding 2 or more single-digit numbers

◆ Using numbers and standard notation ($+$, $-$, $=$) to record

Vocabulary

addition

Today's Plan			Materials
ACTIVITY ❶ **Introducing** *Dot Addition*	🕐 15 MIN	👥 CLASS	• M27*; M28*; M29* • T24 🖥 (optional)
ACTIVITY ❷ **Playing** *Dot Addition*	🕐 30 MIN	👥 PAIRS	• M27*; M28*; M29*; M30* (optional)* • Cubes or counters (optional)
DISCUSSION ❸ **Sharing** *Dot Addition* **Sums**	🕐 15 MIN	👥 CLASS	• M28 (completed work) • Chart paper (optional)
SESSION FOLLOW-UP ❹ **Daily Practice**			• *Student Activity Book*, p. 21 • *Student Math Handbook*, p. G5

*See *Materials to Prepare*, p. 69.

Classroom Routines

Quick Survey: Have a brother? Have a sister? **Create a Venn Diagram, entitled** "Do you have a brother? Do you have a sister?", on chart paper. Label the inside of the first circle: "I have a brother", the second circle: "I have a sister" and the overlapping section: "I have a brother and a sister". List students' names in the appropriate section and then count them. After counting the responses, have a short discussion about the results of the survey.

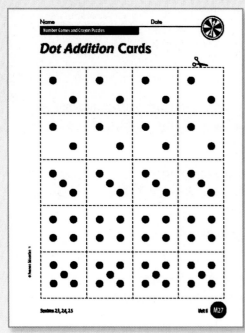

▲ Resource Masters, M27

▲ Resource Masters, M28

ACTIVITY

① Introducing *Dot Addition*

Introduce a new variation of *Dot Addition* by playing a demonstration game with the class. You will need a deck of *Dot Addition* Cards (M27) and *Dot Addition* Gameboard A (M28). Have available copies of Dot Addition (M29) as needed. You may want to use the transparency from Unit 3 (T24).

- Deal out 4 rows of 5 cards, face up, next to *Dot Addition* Gameboard A. Remind students that the object is to make a combination for each number on the gameboard.

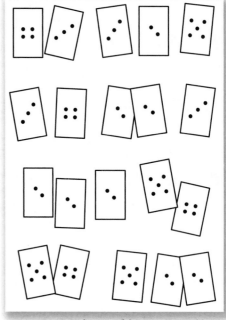

At the start of the game, Dot Addition cards are arranged in rows.

- In Unit 3, players could use a card more than once. In this variation, players cannot use a card twice. For example, if students use three 3-dot cards to make 9, they cannot then use four 3-dot cards to make 12.

- When a number appears twice on a gameboard (as 12 does in this case), students need to find *2 different ways* to make that number. Players can rearrange their cards at any time until they have a completed gameboard.

- Play a demonstration game, asking volunteers to suggest a combination for each number. When you have filled the gameboard, demonstrate recording each combination with addition notation on another copy of Gameboard A. Some students might need or want to also draw the dot images they used.

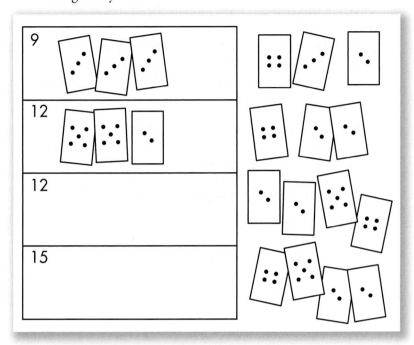

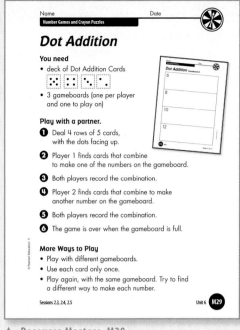

▲ Resource Masters, M29

Cards are moved onto the gameboard to make combinations for each number.

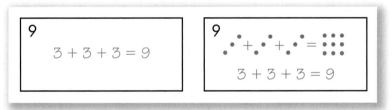

Recording Dot addition

ACTIVITY

30 MIN   PAIRS

2 Playing *Dot Addition*

Students play in pairs (or they can play individually). Pairs work together to find combinations that match the numbers on *Dot Addition* Gameboard A (M28). Students can play on one gameboard and record on their own copy of the gameboard.

Math Note

① Skip Counting Some students may begin counting by 2s or 3s for small quantities, and then switch to 1s as quantities increase. Counting by numbers other than 1 is a skill that develops gradually over the early elementary years. Students will have opportunities to begin making sense of this in Unit 8, *Twos, Fives, and Tens,* and will continue to develop their understanding of this idea in Grades 2 and 3.

ONGOING ASSESSMENT: Observing Students at Work

Dot Addition provides practice decomposing a number in many ways ($12 = 5 + 5 + 2$ or $4 + 4 + 3 + 1$), adding single-digit numbers, and using addition notation to record. This new variation also adds a strategic aspect in that cards can only be used once.

● **How do students find combinations?** Do they work randomly? Begin with one number and count up to see what they need? Look for particular combinations? (*"I know $4 + 5 = 9$, but I don't have a 5 left, so I'll use $2 + 3$."*)

● **How do students add?** Do they count from 1? Count on? Use combinations they know, like doubles or those that make 10? Can they quickly add 1 or 2 to any number?

● **Are any students counting by groups?①**

● **How accurate are students in their use of addition notation?**

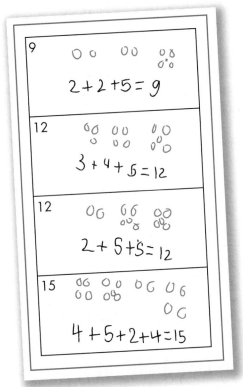

Sample Student Work

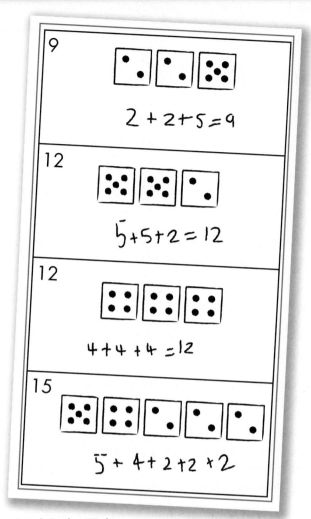

Sample Student Work

▲ Resource Masters, M30

DIFFERENTIATION: Supporting the Range of Learners

Intervention If students are struggling, suggest a combination of cards to start with.

You're trying to make 12. What if we start with 5 and 5, how many does that get us? How many more do we need to make 12?

Cubes or counters can be useful for figuring out such "how many more" questions. If some students are finding the game very difficult, use *Dot Addition* Blank Gameboard (M30) to make them new gameboards with smaller numbers (such as 6, 6, 8, and 8, or 6, 7, 8, and 10).

Extension Challenge students who finish quickly to play again without using any of the same combinations.

Math Notes

② Using Familiar Combinations Some students will be working more randomly, seeing each combination as completely separate. Others will be using what they know about 12, combinations of 12, and combinations of the smaller numbers that make up 12 (e.g., *"I know 6 and 6 is 12. If you split both 6s into 3s you get 3 + 3 + 3 + 3."*). Encourage students whom you have seen using such strategies to share their work.

③ Relationships Among Solutions By asking students to attend to the solutions already recorded, you help them appreciate the importance of keeping track. This, too, can help students begin to notice relationships among different solutions.

Professional Development

④ Teacher Note: Building on Number Combinations You Know, p. 149

DISCUSSION

③ Sharing *Dot Addition* Sums

15 MIN   CLASS

Math Focus Points for Discussion

◆ Adding 2 or more single digit numbers

Call students together to discuss the new variation of *Dot Addition*. Students will need the copy of the gameboard on which they recorded their work.

What did you think of the new *Dot Addition* rule? Is it harder or easier to play when you can only use each card once?

Collect the different combinations of 12 that students found, and discuss their strategies for finding combinations of 12.②

When [Vic] made 12 he had [3 + 3 + 3 + 3]. Did anyone else get that? [Vic], how did you figure out that [3 + 3 + 3 + 3] worked for 12?

For each combination that is shared, ask 2 or 3 students to prove that it equals 12.

[Vic] knew that [3 + 3 is 6 and 3 + 3 is 6, and 6 + 6 is 12]. Does anyone have a *different* way to show that [3 + 3 + 3 + 3 is 12]? [Emilia] thought [three 3s is 9, 1 more is 10, and 2 more than 10 is 12]. Who has another way?

Model ways to record the different strategies students used to combine the numbers. By sharing and modeling such strategies, students will increasingly recognize relationships among combinations.③

Before sharing a new combination, ask students to check to see whether it is already listed. Note that students may disagree about whether combinations that use the same addends in different order (such as 4 + 3 + 3 and 3 + 4 + 3) are "the same." Discuss what is the same and what is different about such combinations, and then decide together whether to include both on your list.④

If students suggest combinations of 12 that cannot be made with *Dot Addition* Cards (such as 2 + 2 + 8), you might decide to record those as well, perhaps in a different list.

Dot Addition: Combinations of 12	
Combinations with Dot Cards	**Other Combinations**
5 + 4 + 3 4 + 3 + 5 3 + 4 + 5	6 + 4 + 2
5 + 5 + 2	1 + 1 + 1 + 1 + 1 + 1 + 1 + 1 + 1 + 1 + 1 + 1
5 + 3 + 2 + 2	
	8 + 2 + 2
2 + 2 + 2 + 2 + 2 + 2	
4 + 4 + 4	
4 + 4 + 2 + 2	
3 + 3 + 3 + 3	
4 + 3 + 3 + 2	

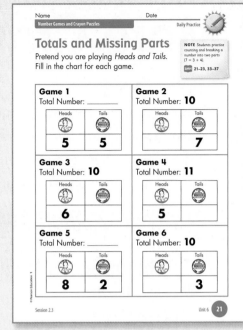

▲ **Student Activity Book, p. 21**

SESSION FOLLOW-UP
4 Daily Practice

 Daily Practice: For ongoing review, have students complete *Student Activity Book* page 21.

 Student Math Handbook: Students and families may use *Student Math Handbook* page G5 for reference and review. See pages 189–195 in the back of this unit.

More Crayon Puzzles

Math Focus Points

◆ Reasoning about more, less, and equal amounts

◆ Finding a solution that fits several clues

◆ Finding combinations of numbers up to 20

◆ Adding 2 or more single-digit numbers

Today's Plan	Materials
① MATH WORKSHOP **Combinations of Numbers** **①A** Crayon Puzzles **①B** *Dot Addition* 🕐 45 MIN	**①A** • *Student Activity Book,* pp. 17–18 (from Session 2.2); pp. 22–23 • M31–M36, (optional)* • Red and blue connecting cubes or color tiles; green connecting cubes (optional) **①B** • Materials from Session 2.3, p. 81 • M37–M38* (optional)*
② DISCUSSION **Sharing a Crayon Puzzle** 🕐 15 MIN 👪 CLASS	• *Student Activity Book,* p. 18 (completed work) • Chart paper (optional)
③ SESSION FOLLOW-UP **Daily Practice and Homework**	• *Student Activity Book,* pp. 24–25 • *Student Math Handbook,* pp. 46–47, 48–49; G5

*See *Materials to Prepare,* p. 69.

Classroom Routines

Start With/Get To Counting Forward Choose the *start with* number from the first basket (cards 1–50) and the *get to* number from the second (cards 51–100). Ask students to find and mark both numbers on the number line. As a class, count from the *start with* number to the *get to* number.

MATH WORKSHOP

Combinations of Numbers

45 MIN

The discussion at the end of this session will focus on Crayon Puzzle 3 (7 crayons with more red than blue) on *Student Activity Book* page 18. Once students have solved this puzzle and recorded their work, they can choose to continue working on Crayon Puzzles or they can play *Dot Addition*.

1A Crayon Puzzles

INDIVIDUALS   PAIRS

Students continue to solve crayon puzzles in which there are *more* crayons of one color than the other. If students have completed *Student Activity Book* pages 17–18 (from Session 2.2), they should solve problems on *Student Activity Book* pages 22–23.

ONGOING ASSESSMENT: Observing Students at Work

For information about observing and supporting students at work on Crayon Puzzles About More, see Session 2.2, page 78.

DIFFERENTIATION: Supporting the Range of Learners

Extension Students who complete the crayon puzzles on the *Student Activity Book* pages and are engaged and excited by them may be interested in solving Challenging Crayon Puzzles (M31–M36). These pages provide additional types of puzzles, including puzzles about *fewer, most, fewest,* and puzzles that have only one answer.

1B Dot Addition

PAIRS

For complete details about this game, see Session 2.3, pages 82–85.

Professional Development

 Teacher Note: About Crayon Puzzles, p. 147

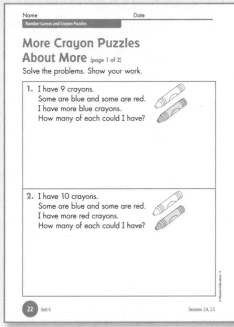

Name _____ Date _____
Number Games and Crayon Puzzles

More Crayon Puzzles
About More (page 1 of 2)
Solve the problems. Show your work.

1. I have 9 crayons.
   Some are blue and some are red.
   I have more blue crayons.
   How many of each could I have?

2. I have 10 crayons.
   Some are blue and some are red.
   I have more red crayons.
   How many of each could I have?

22   Unit 6   Sessions 2.4, 2.5

▲ Student Activity Book, p. 22

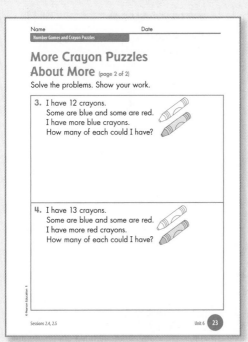

Name _____ Date _____
Number Games and Crayon Puzzles

More Crayon Puzzles
About More (page 2 of 2)
Solve the problems. Show your work.

3. I have 12 crayons.
   Some are blue and some are red.
   I have more blue crayons.
   How many of each could I have?

4. I have 13 crayons.
   Some are blue and some are red.
   I have more red crayons.
   How many of each could I have?

Sessions 2.4, 2.5   Unit 6   23

▲ Student Activity Book, p. 23

Resource Masters, M31–M36

Resource Masters, M37

DIFFERENTIATION: Supporting the Range of Learners

Extension Students can play on Gameboards B and C (M37–M38), which offer different totals.

Students may begin to count by 2s, 3s, or even 5s as they practice playing Dot Addition.

DISCUSSION

2 Sharing a Crayon Puzzle

15 MIN   CLASS

Math Focus Points for Discussion

◆ Reasoning about more, less, and equal amounts

◆ Finding a solution that fits several clues

Students will need their copy of *Student Activity Book* page 18 for this discussion.

Read Puzzle 3 aloud.

I have 7 crayons. Some are blue and some are red. I have *more* red crayons. How many of each could I have?

As in Session 2.2 (page 79), ask students for strategies and solutions.

Then ask students to consider what should by now be a familiar question.

Do you think we have found *all* of the combinations that fit the clues?

Because of the habits established in the How Many of Each? work over the course of the year, some students may already be asking themselves this question as they work.

Professional Development

❷ **Dialogue Box:** I Think There's Only 3 Ways, p. 177

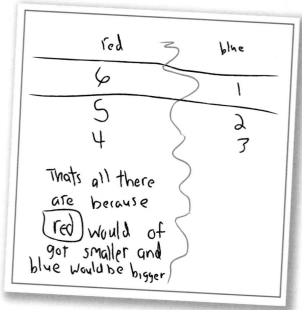

Sample Student Work

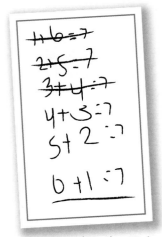

Sample Student Work

Others will be ready to discuss it with their classmates. ❷

▲ **Resource Masters, M38**

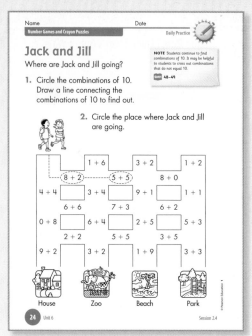

▲ Student Activity Book, p. 24

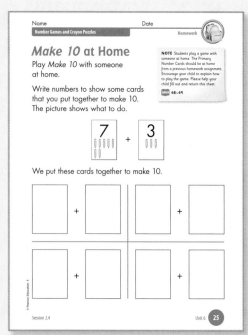

▲ Student Activity Book, p. 25

Students might say:

"You can't go under 4 because then we would have more blue than red and that doesn't fit the rule."

"We can't go over 6 for the red because there has to be 7 crayons."

SESSION FOLLOW-UP

 3 Daily Practice and Homework

 Daily Practice: For reinforcement of this unit's content, have students complete *Student Activity Book* page 24.

Homework: Students play *Make 10* with someone at home. If you assigned this homework in Investigation 1 (Session 1.4), then students will already have the materials they need at home. Tell students that the person with whom they play the game can help them complete *Student Activity Book* page 25. Remind students to return the page to class.

Student Math Handbook: Students and families may use *Student Math Handbook* pages 46–47, 48–49 and G5 for reference and review. See pages 189–195 in the back of this unit.

Assessment: Ten Crayons in All

Math Focus Points

◆ Finding as many 2-addend combinations of 10 as possible

◆ Reasoning about more, less, and equal amounts

◆ Adding 2 or more single-digit numbers

Today's Plan	Materials
ASSESSMENT ACTIVITY **① Ten Crayons in All** ✔ 🕐 20 MIN 👤 INDIVIDUALS	• M39* • Counters and other tools
MATH WORKSHOP **② Combinations of Numbers** 🕐 40 MIN **2A Crayon Puzzles** **2B Dot Addition**	**2A** • *Student Activity Book,* pp. 22–23 (from Session 2.4) • M31–M36 (from Session 2.4; optional) • Red and blue connecting cubes or color tiles; green connecting cubes (optional) **2B** • Materials from Session 2.3, p. 81 • M37*–M38* (from Session 2.4; optional); M40–M41 (optional)*
SESSION FOLLOW-UP **③ Daily Practice**	• *Student Activity Book,* p. 27 • *Student Math Handbook,* pp. 46–47, 48–49, G5

*See *Materials to Prepare,* p. 69.

Classroom Routines

Morning Meeting How Many Days . . . ? Follow your daily *Morning Meeting* Routine. During *Calendar,* have students use the calendar to determine how many days until a class event or holiday that will happen this month. Ask students to share their strategies.

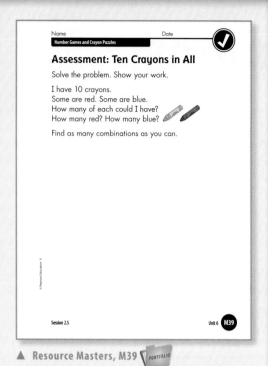

Ten Crayons in All

20 MIN INDIVIDUALS

Explain that students will be solving a How Many of Each? problem today. Because you would like to get a sense of how much students have grown in their math thinking so far this year, they will work individually. ❷

Here's the problem. There are 10 crayons in a box. Some are red and some are blue. What combinations of crayons could I have in my crayon box? How many reds? How many blues? Remember, I need 10 crayons in all.

Try to find all the combinations of 10 red and blue crayons. You should find at least 5 combinations.

Remind students that they may use counters or other classroom tools to help them, and encourage them to use numbers and equations to record their work on Assessment: Ten Crayons in All (M39).

▲ Resource Masters, M39 PORTFOLIO

Professional Development

❶ **Teacher Note:** Assessment: Ten Crayons in All, p. 151

Teaching Note

❷ **Assessing Benchmark 1** As they solve this How Many of Each problem, students are assessed on their ability to find at least five 2-addend combinations of 10.

As the teacher circulates during the assessment activity, she observes some students working systematically to solve the problem.

ONGOING ASSESSMENT: Observing Students at Work

Students find many 2-addend combinations of 10. This problem allows you to assess students' growth with How Many of Each? problems. It also provides an opportunity to get an initial sense of how familiar students are with the combinations of 10. Fluency with these combinations is expected by the end of Unit 8, *Twos, Fives, and Tens.*❶

- **How do students model and solve the problem?** Do they find at least 5 combinations of 10? Do they find them all?

- **Are students working more systematically?** Do they work "in order" or use "opposites" to generate combinations, or do they work more randomly? How do students explain why they think they have found them all?

- **How do students record their work?** How accurately do they use addition notation?

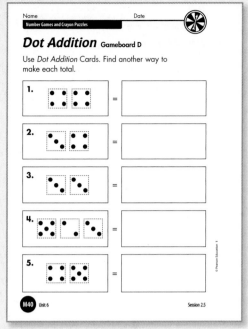

▲ **Resource Masters, M40**

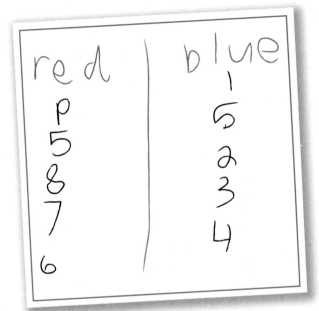

Sample Student Work

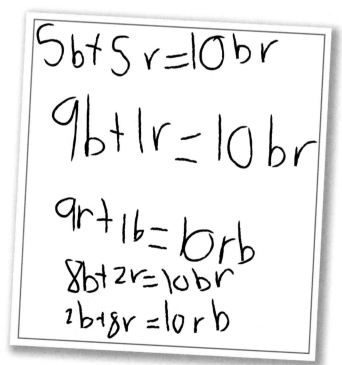

Sample Student Work

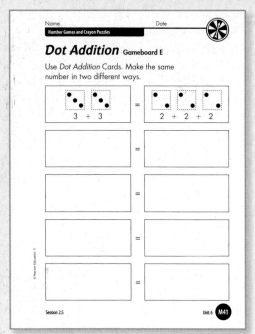

▲ Resource Masters, M41

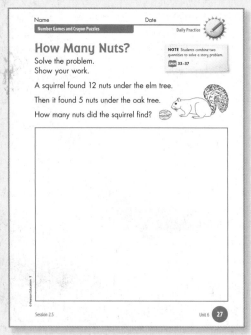

▲ Student Activity Book, p. 27

MATH WORKSHOP
2 Combinations of Numbers

40 MIN

As they finish the assessment, students choose between solving crayon puzzles or playing *Dot Addition*.

2A Crayon Puzzles

INDIVIDUALS   PAIRS

For complete details about this activity, see Session 2.2, pages 77–80.

2B *Dot Addition*

PAIRS

For complete details about this game, see Session 2.3, pages 82–85.

DIFFERENTIATION: Supporting the Range of Learners

Extension Students who have already played on Gameboards B and C (M37–M38) can play on Gameboards D and E (M40–M41). Gameboard D asks students to find another way to make each total. Gameboard E challenges students to make the same number in 2 different ways.

SESSION FOLLOW-UP
3 Daily Practice

Daily Practice: For ongoing review, have students complete *Student Activity Book* page 27.

Student Math Handbook: Students and families may use *Student Math Handbook* pages 46–47, 48–49, G5 for reference and review. See pages 189–195 in the back of this unit.

Mathematical Emphases

Whole Number Operations Making sense of and developing strategies to solve addition and subtraction problems with small numbers

Math Focus Points

◆ Adding 2 or more single-digit numbers

◆ Visualizing, retelling, and modeling the action in addition and subtraction (removal) situations

◆ Subtracting one number from another, with initial totals of up to 12

◆ Developing strategies for solving addition and subtraction story problems

◆ Solving addition and subtraction story problems

Whole Number Operations Using manipulatives, drawings, tools, and notation to show strategies and solutions

Math Focus Points

◆ Using numbers and standard notation $(+, -, =)$ to record

◆ Developing strategies for recording solutions to story problems

Addition and Subtraction

	Student Activity Book	Student Math Handbook	Professional Development: Read Ahead of Time	
SESSION 3.1 p. 102				
Five-in-a-Row with Three Cards Students learn and play a variation of a familiar game, *Five-in-a-Row*. In this version, they have three numbers and can cover the sum of any two. The session ends with the class solving several addition story problems.	28	33–37; G11	• **Dialogue Box:** An Addition Story Problem Aloud, p. 179	
SESSION 3.2 p. 107				
Subtraction Games Students revisit subtraction variations of *Roll and Record* and *Five-in-a-Row,* and then solve several subtraction story problems.	29–31	38–42; G10, G20	• **Dialogue Box:** A Subtraction Story Problem Aloud, p. 181	
SESSION 3.3 p. 112				
Assessment: Counting On Students practice adding and subtracting single-digit numbers and then solve several story problems as a class. In this and the next several sessions, individual students' strategies for combining single-digit numbers are assessed during Math Workshop.	33	33–37, 38–42; G10, G11, G20	• **Teacher Note:** Assessment: Counting On, p. 154	
SESSION 3.4 p. 116				
Addition and Subtraction Story Problems Students listen to, retell, and solve several addition and subtraction story problems as a class and then individually, on paper.	34–38	38–42	• **Teacher Notes:** Three Approaches to Story Problems, p. 156; Supporting Students as They Solve Story Problems, p. 159; Supporting Students as They Record Story Problem Work, p. 161	

Morning Meeting

- **Calendar** Display the calendar showing class events and holidays. (from Investigation 2)
- **Monthly Weather Data Chart**
- **Yearly Weather Data Chart**

Start With/Get To

- **Baskets and pocket 100 chart**
- ***Start With/Get To* Cards** (from Investigation 2)

Quick Images

- **T45, Ten-Frame Cards** Gather the envelope with transparencies. (from Investigation 2)

Quick Surveys

- **Chart** Prepare a 3-column table titled "Which day do you like best?" on chart paper. Label the columns "Monday," "Tuesday," and "Wednesday."

Materials to Gather	Materials to Prepare
• **Primary Number Cards** (1 deck per pair; from Investigation 1) • **T46, *Five-in-a-Row with Three Cards* Gameboard A** • **Counters** (about 20 per pair) • **Cubes or counters** (as needed for story problems) • **Chart paper** (optional)	• **M42, *Five-in-a-Row with Three Cards* Gameboard A** Make copies. You may wish to make copies on cardstock and laminate the gameboards. (1 per pair) • **M43, *Five-in-a-Row with Three Cards*** Make copies. (as needed)
• **T27, *Five-in-a-Row: Subtraction*** • **T26, Roll and Record: Subtraction Recording Sheet** • **Connecting cubes** (12 per student or pair) • **Counters** (15 per pair to use as game markers) • **Dot cubes and number cubes with numerals 7–12** (1 per pair) • **Cubes or counters** (as needed for story problems) • **Chart paper** (optional)	• **M44, *Five-in-a-Row: Subtraction* Gameboard** Make copies. You may wish to make copies on cardstock and laminate the gameboards. (1 per student or pair) • **M45, *Five-in-a-Row: Subtraction*** Make copies. (as needed) • **M46, *Roll and Record: Subtraction* Recording Sheet** Make copies for use throughout this Investigation. (as needed in this session; then 1 per student in subsequent sessions) • **M47, *Roll and Record: Subtraction*** Make copies. (as needed) • **Number cubes with numerals 7–12** Use blank cubes and labels to make number cubes with the numerals 7–12. (1 cube per pair)
• **Cubes or counters** (as needed for story problems) • **Chart paper** (optional) • **Materials for *Five-in-a-Row: Subtraction* and *Roll and Record: Subtraction*** See Session 3.2. • **Materials for *Five-in-a-Row with Three Cards*** See Session 3.1. • **Dot cube and number cubes with numerals 1–6** (2 per class; optional)	• **M48, Assessment Checklist: *Counting On*** Make copies. (2–3 per class) • **M49–M50, *Five-in-a-Row with Three Cards* Gameboards B and C** Make copies. You may wish to make copies on cardstock and laminate the gameboards. (as needed; optional)
• **Cubes or counters** (as needed) • **Chart paper** (optional)	

 Overhead Transparency   Checklist Available

Addition and Subtraction,
continued

	Student Activity Book	Student Math Handbook	Professional Development: Read Ahead of Time	
SESSION 3.5 p. 120				
Solving Story Problems Students continue to solve addition and subtraction story problems and record their work. Class discussion focuses on strategies for adding and subtracting.	34–37 39–40	33–37, 38–42, 44–45	• **Teacher Note:** The Relationship Between Addition and Subtraction, p. 163 • **Dialogue Box:** Discussing Addition Strategies, p. 183; Naming and Comparing Strategies for Subtracting, p. 185; Does This Show Paula's Strategy?, p. 187	
SESSION 3.6 p. 128				
Strategies for Adding Students solve story problems and play addition and subtraction games. Class discussion focuses on strategies for adding.	34–37 41	33–37; G10, G11, G20		
SESSION 3.7 p. 131				
Strategies for Subtracting Students complete their work on addition and subtraction story problems and games. Class discussion focuses on strategies for subtracting.	34–37, 42	33–37, 48–49; G10, G11, G20		
SESSION 3.8 p. 134				
End-of-Unit Assessment Students solve 2 story problems as an assessment.	43	33–37, 38–42	• **Teacher Note:** End-of-Unit Assessment, p. 164	

Materials to Gather	Materials to Prepare
• **Cubes or counters (as needed)**	• **Chart paper** Label one sheet of chart paper "Strategies for Adding " and another sheet "Strategies for Subtracting."
• **M48, Assessment Checklist:** *Counting On* ☑ • **Cubes or counters** (as needed) • **Materials for** *Five-in-a-Row: Subtraction* **and** *Roll and Record: Subtraction* See Session 3.2. • **Materials for** *Five-in-a-Row with Three Cards* See Session 3.1. For variation, use Gameboards B and C (M49 and M50). • **Chart: "Strategies for Adding"** (from Session 3.5)	• **M51–M54, Challenging Story Problems** Make copies. (as needed; optional)
• **Materials for** *Story Problems* See Session 3.6. • **M48, Assessment Checklist:** *Counting On* (from Session 3.3) ☑ • **Materials for** *Five-in-a-Row: Subtraction* **and** *Roll and Record: Subtraction* See Session 3.2. • **Materials for** *Five-in-a-Row with Three Cards* See Session 3.1. • **Chart: "Strategies for Subtracting"** (from Session 3.5)	
• **Cubes or counters** (as needed)	• **M55, End-of-Unit Assessment** Make copies. (1 per student)

☑ Checklist Available

Five-in-a-Row with Three Cards

Math Focus Points

◆ Adding 2 or more single-digit numbers

◆ Visualizing, retelling, and modeling the action in an addition situation

Vocabulary

sum
add

Today's Plan		Materials
ACTIVITY 1 Introducing *Five-in-a-Row with Three Cards*	15 MIN · CLASS	• T46 • Primary Number Cards; counters (as needed); chart paper (optional)
ACTIVITY 2 Playing *Five-in-a-Row with Three Cards*	30 MIN · PAIRS	• M42*, M43 (as needed) • Primary Number Cards; counters (about 20 per pair)
ACTIVITY 3 Addition Story Problems	15 MIN · CLASS	• Cubes or counters (as needed); chart paper (optional)
SESSION FOLLOW-UP 4 Daily Practice		• *Student Activity Book,* p. 28 • *Student Math Handbook,* pp. 33–37; G11

*See *Materials to Prepare,* p. 99.

Classroom Routines

Quick Survey: Monday, Tuesday, or Wednesday? Post the question "Which day do you like best: Monday, Tuesday, or Wednesday?" on chart paper. Record students' responses beneath the question with an "m", "t", or "w" and then count them. After counting the responses, briefly discuss the results of the survey.

ACTIVITY

1 Introducing *Five-in-a-Row with Three Cards*

15 MIN   CLASS

Explain that today students will play a new variation of the game *Five-in-a-Row,* which they have played in previous units. Play a sample game with a volunteer.

Display the transparency of *Five-in-a-Row with Three Cards* Gameboard A (T46). Turn over the top 3 cards from a deck of Primary Number Cards (M13–M16), and record the numbers chosen on a separate piece of paper.

On each turn, players turn over 3 cards. [Stacy] and I picked a [3, a 7, and 1]. Now we can cover the sum of *any two* of these numbers. There are a few ways to add these numbers. [Stacy], what two numbers should we add first? (*3 + 7*) [Stacy] added [3 + 7] and got [10].

Record an equation to show the first sum. Then ask students to find other sums of two of the three numbers. Record an equation for each sum.

Explain that players can cover any square that has one of their sums with a counter. With these cards, players could place a counter on 10, 4, or 8. Be clear that players can cover only one square on each turn. Ask your volunteer to choose a sum to cover on the game board.

Turn over three more cards, record them, and again ask students what sums they could make. Deal a hand that will allow you to demonstrate the use of 0 as one of the addends. For example, if a player turns over 0, 4, and 6, the possibilities include $0 + 4$, $0 + 6$, or $4 + 6$.

Remind students that the goal is to work together with their partner to cover 5 squares in a row, horizontally, vertically, or diagonally. Encourage students to think about where they should place the counter to help them make 5 in a row.

Play until everyone understands the game. Be sure to explain that:

- If no moves can be made (all the possible sums are covered), players turn over three more cards.

- If all the cards in the deck have been used, players reshuffle the deck and turn it face-down again.

Teaching Note

❶ **Shuffling the Cards** Suggest that students deal each round into 3 piles. When all the cards are used, stack one pile on top of the other, turn them over, and begin again. No reshuffling is necessary because the triples used the first time through the deck have already been separated.

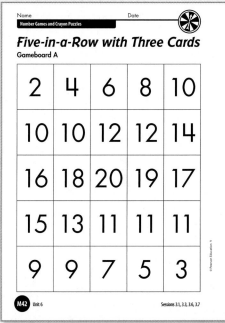

Name _____ Date _____

Number Games and Crayon Puzzles

Five-in-a-Row with Three Cards

Gameboard A

2	4	6	8	10
10	10	12	12	14
16	18	20	19	17
15	13	11	11	11
9	9	7	5	3

M42 Unit 6   Sessions 3.1, 3.3, 3.6, 3.7

▲ **Resource Masters, M42; T46**

The teacher demonstrates turning over 3 cards to begin the game.

The teacher records equations for the 3 cards chosen.

The teacher places a counter on a number matching one of the sums.

ACTIVITY

2 Playing *Five-in-a-Row* with Three Cards

30 MIN   PAIRS

Pairs play *Five-in-a-Row with Three Cards* as you demonstrated. Each pair will need a copy of Gameboard A (M42), a deck of Primary Number Cards (M13–M16), and a collection of counters. Have available copies of *Five-in-a-Row with Three Cards* (M43) as needed.

ONGOING ASSESSMENT: Observing Students at Work

Students practice adding single-digit numbers. They are also reasoning strategically about which sum gives them a better chance of completing a row.

- **How do students add?** Do they count all? Count on? Use knowledge of number combinations? Can they quickly add 1 or 2 to another number?

- **How do students determine which combination of 2 numbers to use?** Do they seem to choose 2 of the numbers at random? Find all the possible combinations and then choose the one they think will help them get 5 in a row?

DIFFERENTIATION: Supporting the Range of Learners

(**Intervention**) Some students may play more reflectively, or strategically, if they record the 3 possible combinations on paper before choosing a square to cover.

ACTIVITY

3 Addition Story Problems

15 MIN   CLASS

In preparation for the story problem work that students will do independently in Sessions 3.4–3.7, the next few sessions will end with the whole class hearing, retelling, and solving several story problems. To begin, pose one or two addition story problems for students to retell and solve as a class. Follow the *Story Problem Routine* that you have been using all year, but add a step where students help you write an equation that represents the problem.

Professional Development

 Dialogue Box: An Addition Story Problem Aloud, p. 179

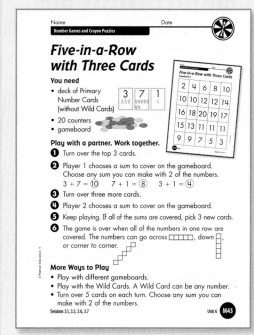

▲ Resource Masters, M43

Algebra Note

 Related Problems When you pose related problems like these, ask students whether anything about the first problem helped them solve the second one. In this set, since one addend increases by 1, the total also increases by 1. Encourage students to explain their ideas and model them with cubes for the whole class as appropriate.

Story Problem Routine

1. Tell students a number story. Encourage them to visualize the action in the story.
2. Ask several students to retell the story. (Or, several students can each tell one part of the story. And occasionally, you might have each student retell the story to a partner.)
3. After retelling each story, ask whether the end result in each case will be more or less than the amount you started with.
4. Ask students to help you write an equation that represents what the problem is asking (e.g., 8 + 4 = ____ or 4 + 8 = ____).
5. Ask students to share strategies for solving the problem, including modeling the problem with cubes or counters.
6. Model methods of recording on chart paper or on the board.

Here are two related problems to use or adapt:

Teo and Paula were playing Five-in-a-Row. *They decided to add 8 and 4. What square did they cover on their game board?*

Lyle and Allie decided to add 8 and 5. What square did they cover on their game board?

SESSION FOLLOW-UP

4 Daily Practice

Daily Practice: For ongoing review, have students complete *Student Activity Book* page 28.

Student Math Handbook: Students and families may use *Student Math Handbook* pages 33–37 and G11 for reference and review. See pages 189–195 in the back of this unit.

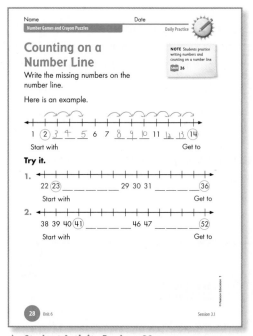

▲ Student Activity Book, p. 28

Subtraction Games

Math Focus Points

◆ Subtracting one number from another, with initial totals of up to 12

◆ Using numbers to record

◆ Visualizing, retelling, and modeling the action in a subtraction (removal) situation

Vocabulary

minus

Today's Plan			Materials
ACTIVITY **① Introducing Subtraction Games**	🕐 15 MIN	👥 CLASS	• T27, M44*; T26, M46*; M45, M47, (as needed)* • Dot cube; number cube with numerals 7–12*; connecting cubes (12 per student or pair)
MATH WORKSHOP **② Playing Subtraction Games** **2A** *Five-in-a-Row: Subtraction* **2B** *Roll and Record: Subtraction*	🕐 30 MIN		**2A** • M44 (1 per student or pair)* • Dot cubes (1 per pair); number cubes with numerals 7–12 (1 per pair)*; counters (15 per pair); connecting cubes (as needed) **2B** • *Student Activity Book*, p. 29 • M46 (as needed)*, M47 (as needed)*
ACTIVITY **③ Solving Subtraction Story Problems**	🕐 15 MIN	👥 CLASS	• Cubes or counters (as needed); chart paper (optional)
SESSION FOLLOW-UP **④ Daily Practice and Homework**			• *Student Activity Book*, pp. 30–31 • *Student Math Handbook*, pp. 38–42; G10, G20

*See *Materials to Prepare*, p. 99.

Classroom Routines

Start With/Get To Counting Forward Choose the *start with* number from the first basket (cards 1–50) and the *get to* number from the second (cards 51–100). Ask students to find and mark both numbers on the number line. As a class, count from the *start with* number to the *get to* number.

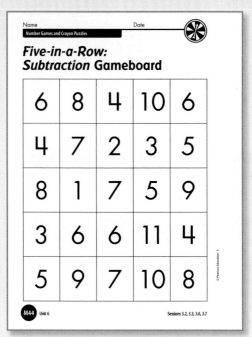

▲ Resource Masters, M44; T27

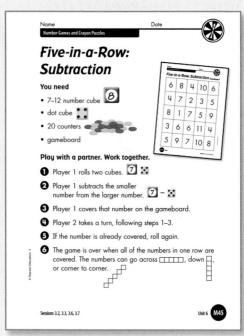

▲ Resource Masters, M45

15 MIN   CLASS

ACTIVITY

① Introducing Subtraction Games

Students played these variations of *Five-in-a-Row* and *Roll and Record* in Unit 3, *Solving Story Problems.* Remind students that both of these games use a dot cube and a number cube with numerals 7–12. Give each student or pair 12 connecting cubes and play a few sample rounds using the transparencies of *Five-in-a-Row: Subtraction* Gameboard (T27) and *Roll and Record: Subtraction* (T26) to reintroduce the games. Explain that players roll both cubes and subtract the number on the dot cube from the number on the number cube.

I rolled a 4 and a 10. In these games you take away the smaller number from the larger number. So what is the problem I need to solve? (10 – 4) The answer to 10 minus 4 will tell us what number to cover on our *Five-in-a-Row* gameboard (or what number to write on our *Roll and Record* recording sheet). How can we figure out how much 10 minus 4 is?

Ask a few students to share how they would solve this problem. Many students will use the cubes or their fingers to model the problem. Others will count back mentally, on their fingers, on the number line, or on the recording sheet. A few may use an addition fact they know, or count up from 4 to 10, to solve the problem.

Students might say:

"I would use my fingers. There's 10. So I would go 9 [one finger down], 8 [second finger down], 7 [third finger down], 6 [fourth finger down]. So 6 are left."

"You can count back from 10 on the number line. Find 10 and then go back like this 9, 8, 7, 6."

"I know another way. You can count up on the number line. You start with 4 and count up 5, 6, 7, 8, 9, 10. That's 6 jumps, so the answer's 6."

[Talisa] said she would make a tower of 10 cubes and take away 4 cubes. Then she would count how many cubes are left. What number would we cover on our *Five-in-a-Row* gameboard [or write on our *Roll and Record* recording sheet]?

Continue with other examples until students understand how to play each game as well as how to record for *Roll and Record: Subtraction.*

MATH WORKSHOP

② Playing Subtraction Games

30 MIN

Students spend Math Workshop playing the subtraction games.

②A *Five-in-a-Row: Subtraction*

PAIRS

Pairs take turns rolling a dot cube and a number cube. They subtract the smaller number (on the dot cube) from the larger number (on the number cube) and use a counter to cover the result on their gameboard. The goal is to cover an entire row—horizontally, vertically, or diagonally. Partners can play cooperatively on one *Five-in-a-Row: Subtraction* gameboard (M44), or students can play on their own gameboard. Have available copies of *Five-in-a-Row: Subtraction* (M45) as needed.

As the teacher circulates during Math Workshop, she observes students using different strategies to subtract one number from another.

✔ ONGOING ASSESSMENT: Observing Students at Work

Students practice subtracting one number from another.

- **Can students determine the problem a given roll represents?** For example, if they roll 3 and 7, do they know they need to solve $7 - 3$?

- **Do students use tools such as counters, their fingers, or the number line to solve the problems?**

- **What strategies do students use?** Do they count all? Count up or back? Use an addition combination they know? (e.g., *I know* $3 + 4 = 7$, *so* $7 - 3 = 4$.)

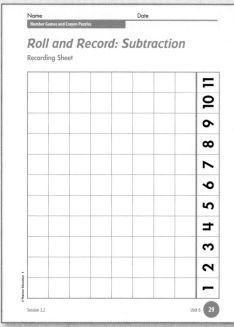

▲ Student Activity Book, p. 29; Resource Masters, M46; T26

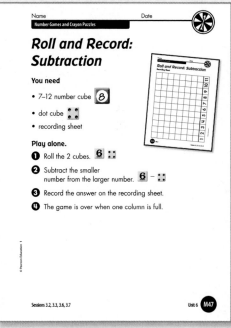

▲ Resource Masters, M47

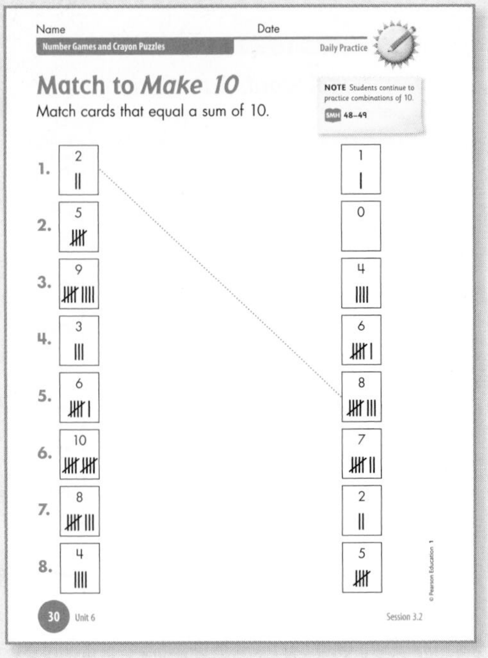
Name Date
Number Games and Crayon Puzzles
Daily Practice

Match to *Make 10*

Match cards that equal a sum of 10.

NOTE Students continue to practice combinations of 10.
SMH 48–49

1.	2	1
2.	5	0
3.	9	4
4.	3	6
5.	6	8
6.	10	7
7.	8	2
8.	4	5

© Pearson Education 1

30 Unit 6 Session 3.2

▲ Student Activity Book, p. 30

- **How do students decide which numbers to cover on their gameboard?** Are they playing strategically?

DIFFERENTIATION: Supporting the Range of Learners

Intervention Some students will need support determining the problem to solve after rolling the dot cube and number cube. Ask students to tell you which cube shows the larger number.

So if we have [8], and take away [4], then how much would we have?

Encourage students to use cubes or counters to model the action of the problem as needed.

Extension Students who are ready for more challenge can roll 1 number cube and 2 dot cubes, and decide which subtraction problem to solve. For example, if they roll 12, 6, and 5, they can cover the number 6 on the gameboard (12 – 6) or the number 7 (12 – 5).

2B *Roll and Record: Subtraction*

PAIRS

Pairs take turns rolling a dot cube and a number cube, and subtracting the smaller number (on the dot cube) from the larger number (on the number cube). Players record the result on their own copy of *Student Activity Book* page 29. Have available copies of *Roll and Record: Subtraction* (M47) as needed.①

ONGOING ASSESSMENT: Observing Students at Work

Students practice subtracting one number from another, and using numbers to record. See section 2A above for information about what to look for as you observe students at work. Also take note of students' number writing skills.

- **Are students able to accurately and legibly record the results?**

DIFFERENTIATION: Supporting the Range of Learners

Intervention See suggestions in section 2A above.

Extension Students who are ready for more challenge can record the subtraction expressions on *Student Activity Book* page 29, rather than recording the answers.

ACTIVITY

3 Solving Subtraction Story Problems

15 MIN   CLASS

Today, pose several subtraction story problems for students to retell and solve as a whole class. Follow the *Story Problem Routine* that you established in Session 3.1, page 106.

Here are 2 problems to use or adapt:

Felipe was playing Roll and Record: Subtraction. *He rolled a 12 and a 6. What number did he record on his gameboard?*

Sacha was playing Five-in-a-Row: Subtraction. *She rolled a 12 and a 7. What number did she cover on her gameboard?*

SESSION FOLLOW-UP

4 Daily Practice and Homework

Daily Practice: For reinforcement of this unit's content, have students complete *Student Activity Book* page 30.

Homework: Students complete a *Dot Addition* gameboard for homework, recording in each row on *Student Activity Book* page 31.

Student Math Handbook: Students and families may use *Student Math Handbook* pages 38–42 and G10, G20 for reference and review. See pages 189–195 in the back of this unit.

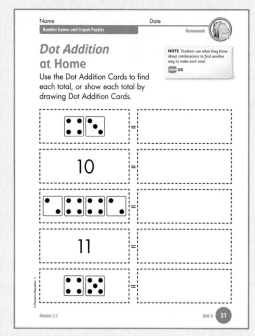

▲ **Student Activity Book, p. 31**

Assessment: Counting On

Math Focus Points

◆ Adding 2 or more single-digit numbers

◆ Visualizing, retelling, and modeling the action in a subtraction (removal) situation

◆ Subtracting one number from another, with initial totals of up to 12

Vocabulary

count on

Today's Plan		Materials
MATH WORKSHOP **① Addition and Subtraction Games** **①A** *Five-in-a-Row: Subtraction* **①B** *Roll and Record: Subtraction* **①C** Assessment: *Counting On* *Five-in-a-Row with Three Cards*	45 MIN	**①A** • Materials from Session 3.2, p. 107 **①B** • Materials from Session 3.2, p. 107 Use M46 in place of *Student Activity Book*, p. 29 **①C** • Materials from see Session 3.1, p. 102 • M48* ☑ ; M49–M50* (optional) • Dot cubes (optional); number cubes with numerals 1–6 (optional)
ACTIVITY **② More Story Problems**	15 MIN CLASS	• Cubes or counters (as needed); chart paper (optional)
SESSION FOLLOW-UP **③ Daily Practice**		• *Student Activity Book*, p. 33 • *Student Math Handbook*, pp. 33–37, 38–42; G10, G11, G20

*See *Materials to Prepare*, p. 99.

Classroom Routines

Quick Images: Ten Frames Show transparencies of three Ten-Frame Cards (T45) with two that total 10. Begin with 7, 3, and 2. Follow the basic *Quick Images* activity. Ask students to determine the total number of dots and to share their strategies. Repeat with the combinations 7, 3, and 4 and then 8, 2, and 1.

MATH WORKSHOP
1 Addition and Subtraction Games

45 MIN

Students choose to play one or more of 3 games that provide practice with subtraction and addition.

By the end of this unit you can expect that students will be able to at least count on to combine 2 small quantities (Benchmark 2). In order to assess this benchmark, meet with each student individually between now and the end of this unit to play a few rounds of *Five-in-a-Row with Three Cards.* Record your observations on Assessment Checklist: *Counting On* (M48).

If you have students who you suspect are counting all because this game is played with Primary Number Cards (M13–M16) that show each quantity, pose several additional problems for them using 1 dot cube and 1 number cube (with numerals 1–6). Roll the cubes several times, asking students to combine the results. Then do the same with 2 number cubes. Record your observations on Assessment Checklist: *Counting On* (M48).

1A *Five-in-a-Row: Subtraction*

PAIRS

For complete details about this game, see Session 3.2, pages 109–110.

1B *Roll and Record: Subtraction*

PAIRS

For complete details about this game, see Session 3.2, page 110.

1C Assessment: *Counting On*
Five-in-a-Row with Three Cards

INDIVIDUALS PAIRS

For complete details about this game, see Session 3.1, pages 103–105. As you circulate, meet with individual students to observe their ability to count on. Record observations on Assessment Checklist: *Counting On* (M48).

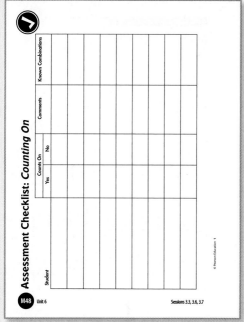

▲ **Resource Masters, M48** ☑

Professional Development
❶ Teacher Note: Assessment: Counting On, p. 154

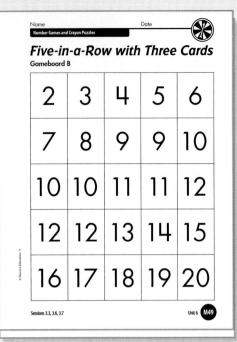

Name _____ Date _____
Number Games and Crayon Puzzles

Five-in-a-Row with Three Cards
Gameboard B

2	3	4	5	6
7	8	9	9	10
10	10	11	11	12
12	12	13	14	15
16	17	18	19	20

Sessions 3.3, 3.6, 3.7   Unit 6 **M49**

▲ **Resource Masters, M49–M50**

Story Problem Routine

1. Tell students a number story. Encourage them to visualize the action in the story.

2. Ask several students to retell the story. (Or, several students can each tell one part of the story. And occasionally, you might have each student retell the story to a partner.)

3. After retelling each story, ask whether the end result in each case will be more or less than the amount you started with.

4. Ask students to help you write an equation that represents what the problem is asking.

5. Ask students to share strategies for solving the problem, including modeling the problem with cubes or counters.

6. Model methods of recording on chart paper or on the board.

DIFFERENTIATION: Supporting the Range of Learners

Extension For more variation, students can use Gameboards B and C (M49–M50) for *Five-in-a-Row with Three Cards*. Students ready for more challenge can use wild cards, which can stand for any number between 0 and 10. They can also turn over 5 cards on each turn and make sums with any 2 of the 5 cards.

During Math Workshop the teacher assesses a student's ability to combine single-digit numbers using the strategy of counting on.

15 MIN   CLASS

ACTIVITY

2 More Story Problems

Pose several addition and subtraction story problems for students to retell and solve as a class. Do not alert students to the type of story they are about to hear; instead, encourage them to listen carefully and imagine the action. Follow the *Story Problem Routine* that you have already established.

Here are some possible problems to use (or adapt):

Talisa went to the store with her dad. She had 13 pennies to spend. She bought one sticker that cost 3 pennies and another sticker that cost 4 pennies. How many pennies did she have left?

A squirrel started collecting acorns for the winter. Yesterday it found 9 acorns. Today it found 8. How many acorns did the squirrel collect so far?

Bruce went out to the garden to pick flowers for his mom's birthday. He picked 4 red flowers, 6 yellow flowers, and 4 white flowers to make a bouquet. How many flowers did Bruce pick?

Stacy had 15 grapes for a snack. She is so generous that she shared her grapes with everyone at her table. She gave 1 grape to Paula, 1 grape to Jacob, 1 grape to Allie, and 1 grape to Deshawn. How many grapes did she have left?

As part of the Story Problem Routine, *the teacher invites a student to model the problem using cubes.*

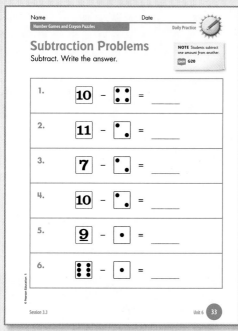

▲ **Student Activity Book, p. 33**

DIFFERENTIATION: Supporting the Range of Learners

ELL Keep in mind the needs of English Language Learners when presenting story problems. Auditory comprehension is improved when there are visuals to support what students are hearing. Act out stories or provide other visual cues to help English Language Learners.

SESSION FOLLOW-UP

3 Daily Practice

 Daily Practice: For reinforcement of this unit's content, have students complete *Student Activity Book* page 33.

 Student Math Handbook: Students and families may use *Student Math Handbook* pages 33–37, 38–42 and G10, G11, G20 for reference and review. See pages 189–195 in the back of this unit.

Addition and Subtraction Story Problems

Math Focus Points

- Developing strategies for solving addition and subtraction story problems
- Developing strategies for recording solutions to story problems
- Using numbers and standard notation (+, −, =) to record

Today's Plan			Materials
ACTIVITY ① **Addition and Subtraction Story Problems**	15 MIN	CLASS	• Cubes or counters (as needed); chart paper (optional)
ACTIVITY ② **Solving Story Problems**	45 MIN	INDIVIDUALS	• *Student Activity Book*, pp. 34–37 • Cubes or counters (as needed)
SESSION FOLLOW-UP ③ **Daily Practice**			• *Student Activity Book*, p. 38 • *Student Math Handbook*, pp. 38–42

Classroom Routines

Start With/Get To Counting Backward In this variation the *start with* basket contains the larger numbers (51–100) and the *get to* basket holds the smaller numbers (1–50). Choose a *start with* number and a *get to* number. Ask students to find and mark both numbers on the number line. As a class, count from the *start with* number backward to the *get to* number.

Addition and Subtraction Story Problems

15 MIN CLASS

Pose several addition and subtraction story problems for students to retell and solve as a class. Do not alert students to the type of story they are about to hear; instead, encourage them to listen carefully and imagine the action. Follow the *Story Problem Routine* that you have already established.

Here are some possible problems to use (or adapt):

Danielle gave her rabbit 13 carrots. The rabbit ate 6 of the carrots in the morning. How many carrots were left?

William loves to collect shells when he goes to the beach. On his last trip, he found 12 periwinkle shells and 3 clam shells. How many shells did he find?

Keena wants to start a sticker collection. For her birthday, her mom gave her 8 stickers. Her uncle gave her 4 stickers. Her brother gave her 2 stickers. How many stickers does Keena have?

Paul had 14 pennies. When he went to the store with his grandmother, he bought a pencil for 4 pennies and an eraser for 5 pennies. How many pennies did he have left?

One step in the Story Problem Routine *involves recording an equation representing the problem.*

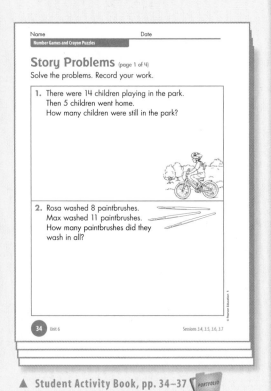

▲ Student Activity Book, pp. 34–37 PORTFOLIO

ACTIVITY

② Solving Story Problems

45 MIN INDIVIDUALS

Story problems will be an activity for the rest of this Investigation. Explain how this will work by revisiting the process you established in Unit 3, *Solving Story Problems,* Session 3.1.

- **Choose a story problem to solve. First try to read the story problem by yourself. The problems have pictures to help you. If there are names in the problems, they will always be Max, Rosa, Kim, or Sam.**

- **If you need help reading the problems, you can get help in different ways. (Explain the process you will use.)** ❶

- **Solve the problem and show your work.**

This student helps another student read the story problem.

There are 8 problems on *Student Activity Book* pages 34–37. Explain that you expect students to use their time wisely, but that you do not expect every student to solve every problem. Students will have 4 days to solve at least 6 or 7 problems. Some students will be able to finish more, and will have an opportunity to solve more challenging problems later in this Investigation.

ONGOING ASSESSMENT: Observing Students at Work

Students read a story problem, determine the action involved, and figure out whether they should add or subtract to solve the problem. Students then solve the problem and show their work.

- **Can students make sense of the action in the problem?**

- **What tools and strategies do students use?**

- **Do students get the right answer?**

- **How do students record their work?**

As you observe students, monitor whether the numbers in the problems seem of average difficulty for most students. You can modify the numbers (smaller and larger) where appropriate.

DIFFERENTIATION: Supporting the Range of Learners

Intervention If students are struggling with a particular problem, reread it together and ask them to tell the story in their own words. Help students think through the situation by asking questions such as:

- How does the story start?

- What happens next?

- Are there more or less at the end of the story than at the beginning?

Encourage students to act out the problem with a partner, to build a model of the situation with counters, and/or to draw pictures of the situation.

SESSION FOLLOW-UP
3 Daily Practice

Daily Practice: For reinforcement of this unit's content, have students complete *Student Activity Book* page 38.

Student Math Handbook: Students and families may use *Student Math Handbook* pages 38–42 for reference and review. See pages 189–195 in the back of this unit.

Professional Development

❷ **Teacher Note:** Three Approaches to Story Problems, p. 156

Math Note

❸ **Key Words** While it can be tempting to teach students to use "key words" in the story to determine the action, this can prevent students from making sense of the action in the problems.

Professional Development

❹ **Teacher Note:** Supporting Students as They Solve Story Problems, p. 159

❺ **Teacher Note:** Supporting Students as They Record Story Problem Work, p. 161

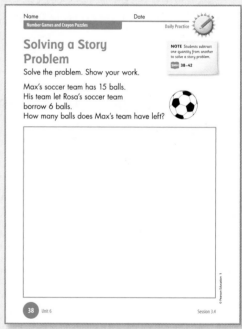

▲ Student Activity Book, p. 38

Solving Story Problems

Math Focus Points

◆ Developing strategies for solving addition and subtraction story problems

◆ Developing strategies for recording solutions to story problems

◆ Using numbers and standard notation (+, −, =) to record

Vocabulary

count back
count up
count all

Today's Plan		Materials
DISCUSSION **① Strategies for Subtraction**	15 MIN CLASS	• *Student Activity Book,* p. 34 (completed work, Problem 1; from Session 3.4) • Chart paper "Strategies for Subtracting"*; cubes or counters (as needed)
ACTIVITY **② Solving Story Problems**	30 MIN INDIVIDUALS	• *Student Activity Book,* pp. 34–37 (from Session 3.4); cubes or counters (as needed)
DISCUSSION **③ Strategies for Addition**	15 MIN CLASS	• *Student Activity Book,* p. 34 (completed work, Problem 2) • Chart paper "Strategies for Adding"*; cubes or counters (as needed)
SESSION FOLLOW-UP **④ Daily Practice and Homework**		• *Student Activity Book,* pp. 39–40 • *Student Math Handbook,* pp. 33–37, 38–42, 44–45

*See *Materials to Prepare,* p. 101.

Classroom Routines

Start With/Get To Counting Backward Choose a *start with* number from the first basket (cards 51–100) and a *get to* number from the second (cards 1–50). Ask students to find and mark both numbers on the number line. As a class, count from the *start with* number backward to the *get to* number.

① DISCUSSION
Strategies for Subtraction

15 MIN   CLASS

Math Focus Points for Discussion

◆ Developing strategies for solving subtraction story problems

◆ Using standard notation (+, −, =) to record

Begin with a brief discussion about Story Problem 1 on *Student Activity Book* page 34. Record students' strategies on a sheet of chart paper labeled "Strategies for Subtracting." Afterward, you can leave this posted in the classroom for children to refer and add to.

Read the story aloud.

There were 14 children playing in the park. Then 5 children went home. How many children were still in the park?

Ask students to help you write an equation that represents what the problem is asking ($14 - 5 =$ ___). Then ask several students, whose strategies represent a range of methods, to explain how they solved the problem.❶

Most students will see this problem as a subtraction situation and remove or take away 5 from 14 (Allie and Carol) or count back 5 from 14 (Bruce). A few students may see this as an adding-on situation and count up from 5. Others may use knowledge of number combinations (Deshawn) and knowledge of the relationship between addition and subtraction (e.g., $14 - 4 = 10$ and $10 - 1 = 9$; or $10 + 5 = 15$ so $9 + 5 = 14$ so $14 - 5$ is 9).❷ ❸

Teaching Note

❶ **Guiding the Discussion** When choosing which strategies to discuss, think about where the majority of your students are in terms of strategies for subtracting. For example, if most students can accurately count all, but few are counting back, you might focus on counting back strategies so that students can try out those strategies over the course of the next few days. There will be another opportunity to discuss subtraction strategies at the end of Session 3.7.

Professional Development

❷ **Teacher Note:** Three Approaches to Story Problems, p. 156

❸ **Teacher Note:** The Relationship Between Addition and Subtraction, p. 163

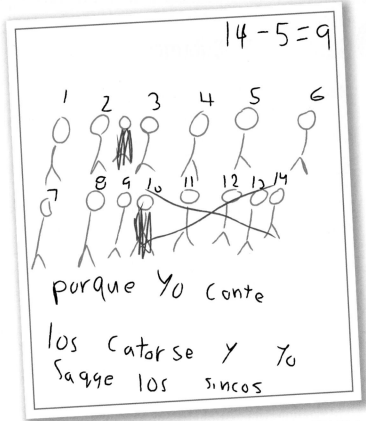

Allie's Work

Translation: because I counted the fourteen and I took out the fives

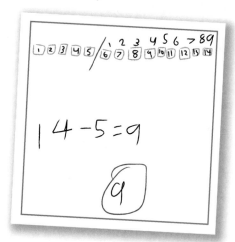

Carol's Work

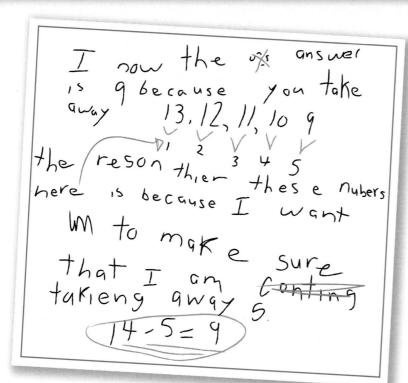

I now the ods answer
is 9 because you take
away 13, 12, 11, 10 9
the reson thier these nubers
here is because I want
wm to make sure
that I am conting
takieng away 5.
14 - 5 = 9

Bruce's Work

if I take away
the 4 from 14
it is 10 take away 1 it is 9
14 — 5 = 9

Deshawn's Work

As you did in *Solving Story Problems* (Unit 3), discuss students' strategies for solving these story problems.

- **Model, discuss, and name the strategy and the tool (if any).** As students share their strategies, model them with cubes, and name the strategies based on the math idea used (e.g., Edgar *counted back,* Danielle *used a combination she knew*). You can also talk with students about any tools they used, such as pictures, cubes or counters, the number line, or their fingers.❹❺

- **Model ways to record.** Many students will still be struggling with *how* to show on paper how they solved a problem, and may choose to record a strategy that is easy to show rather than the one they used. The more you model possible ways to record and discuss representations that match (and do not match) the strategy used, the more students will develop the ability to record accurately and efficiently.❻

- **Continue to discuss efficiency with students.** While some students may still need to draw every item, others will be ready to move to less cumbersome ways of recording their work, such as using tallies instead of drawing the objects in the story, drawing only one picture as a label, and even writing equations.

- **Compare strategies.** Even though many students will still see *counting all* with cubes as different from *counting all* on their fingers or with pictures, continue to push students to think about when and how their strategy is the same as or different from the one shared.

During the discussion this student explains how she solved a subtraction problem using the strategy of counting back on the number line.

ACTIVITY

② Solving Story Problems

30 MIN INDIVIDUALS

Students continue solving the story problems on *Student Activity Book* pages 34–37. See Session 3.4, pages 118–119, for information about observing and supporting students in their work on addition and subtraction story problems.

DISCUSSION

③ Strategies for Addition

15 MIN CLASS

Math Focus Points for Discussion

◆ Developing strategies for solving addition story problems

◆ Using standard notation (+, −, =) to record

At the end of this session, briefly discuss students' strategies for solving Story Problem 2 on *Student Activity Book* page 34. Record students' strategies on a sheet of chart paper labeled "Strategies for Adding." Afterwards, you can leave this posted in the classroom for children to refer to.

Read the story aloud.

Rosa washed 8 paintbrushes. Max washed 11 paintbrushes. How many paintbrushes did they wash in all?

Ask students to help you write an equation that represents what the problem is asking ($8 + 11 = $ ___ or $11 + 8 = $ ___). Then ask several students whose strategies represent a range of methods to explain how they solved the problem.

This discussion should look quite similar to the one that happened at the beginning of this session. Students' strategies for solving this problem will likely include:

- Counting all

- Counting on

- Using number relationships

Students might say:

 "I counted out (drew) 8 cubes. Then I added (drew) 11 more. Then I counted all of them and there were 19."

 "I counted up 8 numbers from 11. 12, 13, 14, 15, 16, 17, 18, 19."

 "I thought of 11 as 10 and 1. Then I did 10 + 8 because I just knew that equaled 18. Plus 1 more is 19."

Again, think about the strategies that most of your students are using to add in order to decide how to focus this discussion. It is likely that many students will benefit from a discussion about counting on, and what it looks like when you count on with cubes, on your fingers, on the number line, or on the 100 chart. Students may also be ready to think about issues of efficiency (e.g., *"Why did Teo start with 11? In the problem, the 8 came first."*).

Note that there will be another discussion about addition strategies at the end of Session 3.6.

During the discussion this student explains how she solved an addition problem using the strategy of counting all.

Daily Practice and Homework

 Daily Practice: For reinforcement of this unit's content, have students complete *Student Activity Book* page 39.

 Homework: Send home *Student Activity Book* page 40, which has one subtraction and one addition story problem for students to solve at home. Remind students to record their solution strategies.

 Student Math Handbook: Students and families may use *Student Math Handbook* pages 33–37, 38–42, 44–45 for reference and review. See pages 189–195 in the back of this unit.

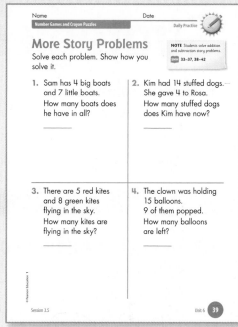

▲ Student Activity Book, p. 39

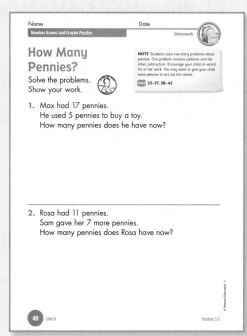

▲ Student Activity Book, p. 40

Strategies for Adding

Math Focus Points

- Developing strategies for solving addition and subtraction story problems
- Using numbers and standard notation (+, −, =) to record
- Developing strategies for recording solutions to story problems

Today's Plan		Materials
MATH WORKSHOP **① Practicing Addition and Subtraction** **①A** Story Problems **①B** *Five-in-a-Row: Subtraction* **①C** *Roll and Record: Subtraction* **①D** Assessment: *Five-in-a-Row with Three Cards*	45 MIN	**①A** • *Student Activity Book,* pp. 34–37 (from Session 3.4) • M51–54, (as needed; optional)* • Cubes or counters (as needed) **①B** • Materials from Session 3.2, p. 107 **①C** • Materials from Session 3.2, p. 107; use M46 in place of *Student Activity Book* p. 29 **①D** • Materials from Session 3.1, p. 102; for variation, use M49–M50 (from Session 3.3) • M48, ☑ (from Session 3.2)
DISCUSSION **② Strategies for Addition**	15 MIN CLASS	• *Student Activity Book,* pp. 34–37 • Chart: "Strategies for Adding" (from Session 3.5); cubes or counters (as needed)
SESSION FOLLOW-UP **③ Daily Practice**		• *Student Activity Book,* p. 41 • *Student Math Handbook,* pp. 33–37; G10, G11, G20

*See *Materials to Prepare,* p. 101.

Classroom Routines

Quick Images: Ten-Frames Show transparencies of three Ten-Frame Cards (T45) with two that total 10. Begin with 6, 4, and 3. Follow the basic *Quick Images* activity. Ask students to determine the total number of dots and to share their strategies. Repeat with the combinations 6, 4, and 7 and then 8, 2, and 6.

MATH WORKSHOP
Practicing Addition and Subtraction

45 MIN

Students continue solving story problems. They can also choose to play the addition and subtraction games introduced earlier in this Investigation.

Continue to meet with students individually, to assess whether they are counting on to add 2 single-digit numbers as they play *Five-in-a-Row with Three Cards.* Record your observations on Assessment Checklist: *Counting On* (M48).

1A Story Problems

INDIVIDUALS

For complete details about this activity, see Session 3.4, pages 118–119.

DIFFERENTIATION: Supporting the Range of Learners

Extension Student who complete *Student Activity Book* pages 34–37 can work on Challenging Story Problems (M51–M54).

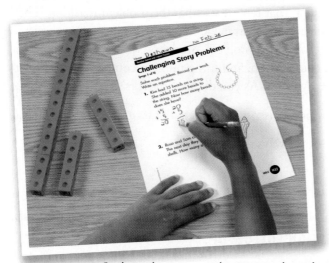

Students who can accurately compute and record can solve challenging story problems during Math Workshop.

1B *Five-in-a-Row: Subtraction*

PAIRS

For complete details about this game, see Session 3.2, pages 109–110.

1C *Roll and Record: Subtraction*

PAIRS

For complete details about this game, see Session 3.2, pages 110–111.

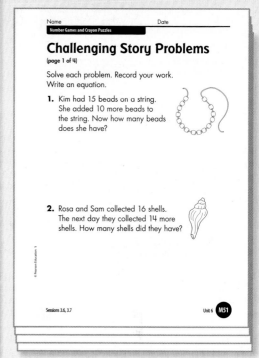

Name _____ Date _____

Number Games and Crayon Puzzles

Challenging Story Problems
(page 1 of 4)

Solve each problem. Record your work.
Write an equation.

1. Kim had 15 beads on a string. She added 10 more beads to the string. Now how many beads does she have?

2. Rosa and Sam collected 16 shells. The next day they collected 14 more shells. How many shells did they have?

Sessions 3.6, 3.7   Unit 6 M51

▲ **Resource Masters, M51–M54**

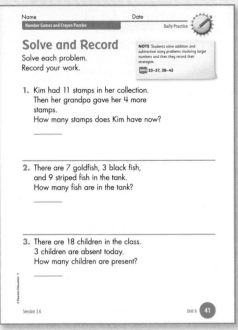

▲ Student Activity Book, p. 41

For complete details about this game, see Session 3.1, pages 103–105.

⒑ Assessment: *Five-in-a-Row with Three Cards*

INDIVIDUALS PAIRS

This activity provides an opportunity for an observed assessment.

---

2 DISCUSSION
Strategies for Addition

15 MIN CLASS

Math Focus Points for Discussion

◆ Developing strategies for solving addition story problems

◆ Using standard notation ($+$, $-$, $=$) to record

Discuss students' strategies for solving another addition story problem. This discussion should be similar to the one at the end of Session 3.5.

Choose a problem and read it aloud. Ask students to help you write an equation that represents what the problem is asking. Then ask several students, whose strategies represent a range of methods, to explain how they solved the problem. Students' strategies will likely include counting all, counting on, and using number combinations or relationships they already know. As you discuss students' strategies, continue to:

• Model, discuss, and name the strategies and the tools used (if any)

• Model ways to record

• Compare strategies

---

3 SESSION FOLLOW-UP
Daily Practice

Daily Practice: For reinforcement of this unit's content, have students complete *Student Activity Book* page 41.

Student Math Handbook: Students and families may use *Student Math Handbook* pages 33–37 and G10, G11, G20 for reference and review. See pages 189–195 in the back of this unit.

Strategies for Subtracting

Math Focus Points

◆ Developing strategies for solving addition and subtraction story problems

◆ Developing strategies for recording solutions to story problems

◆ Using standard notation ($+$, $-$, $=$) to record

◆ Adding and subtracting single-digit numbers

Today's Plan		Materials
① MATH WORKSHOP **Practicing Addition and Subtraction** **①A** Story Problems **①B** *Five-in-a-Row: Subtraction* **①C** *Roll and Record: Subtraction* **①D** Assessment: *Five-in-a-Row with Three Cards*	🕐 **45 MIN**	**①A** • Materials from Session 3.6, p. 128 **①B** • Materials from Session 3.2, p. 107 **①C** • Materials from Session 3.2, p. 107; use M46 in place of *Student Activity Book*, p. 29 **①D** • Materials from Session 3.1, p. 102; for variation, use M49–M50 (from Session 3.3) • M48 ☑ (from Session 3.3)
② DISCUSSION **Strategies for Subtraction**	🕐 **15 MIN** 👥 **CLASS**	• *Student Activity Book*, pp. 34–37 (completed work; from Sessions 3.4–3.6) • Chart: "Strategies for Subtracting" (from Session 3.5); cubes or counters (as needed)
③ SESSION FOLLOW-UP **Daily Practice**		• *Student Activity Book*, p. 42 • *Student Math Handbook*, pp. 33–37, 48–49; G10, G11, G20

Classroom Routines

Start With/Get To Counting Backward Choose a *start with* number from the first basket (cards 51–100) and a *get to* number from the second (cards 1–50). Ask students to find and mark both numbers on the number line. Rather than counting as a whole class, ask students to pair up. Pairs of students can count together or take alternating turns.

Professional Development

 Teacher Note: Assessment: Counting On, p. 154

MATH WORKSHOP

① Practicing Addition and Subtraction

45 MIN

Students continue solving addition and subtraction story problems, and playing addition and subtraction games.

Today is your last chance to assess students as they play *Five-in-a-Row with Three Cards.* Once you have met with every student, review and interpret your notes about strategies that students are using to add single-digit numbers.

1A Story Problems

INDIVIDUALS

For complete details about this activity, see Session 3.4, pages 118–119.

1B *Five-in-a-Row: Subtraction*

PAIRS

For complete details about this game, see Session 3.2, pages 109–110.

1C *Roll and Record: Subtraction*

PAIRS

For complete details about this game, see Session 3.2, pages 110–111.

1D Assessment: *Five-in-a-Row with Three Cards*

INDIVIDUALS PAIRS

For complete details about this game, see Session 3.1, pages 103–105. This activity provides an opportunity for an observed assessment.

DISCUSSION

② Strategies for Subtraction

15 MIN   CLASS

Math Focus Points for Discussion

◆ Developing strategies for solving addition and subtraction story problems

◆ Using standard notation (+, −, =) to record

At the end of this session, discuss students' strategies for solving another subtraction story problem. This discussion should be quite similar to the one that happened at the beginning of Session 3.5.

Choose a problem and read it aloud. Ask students to help you write an equation that represents what the problem is asking. Then ask several students, whose strategies represent a range of methods, to explain how they solved the problem.

Most students will see subtraction story problems as "take away" situations and use strategies that rely on taking one part away from the total amount. For example, these students count all, count back or down, or take away one number from the other in chunks.

Other students may interpret these problems as:

- Adding on situations (*How many do I need to add on to (6) to get to (11)?*)

- Distance or difference situations (*How far is it from (6) to (11)?*)

These students count up, by 1s or in groups, or reason about addition combinations they know and about the relationship between addition and subtraction (*If 6 + 5 = 11 then 11 − 6 = 5*).

As you discuss students' strategies, continue to:

- Model, discuss, and name the strategies and the tools used (if any)

- Model ways to record

- Compare strategies

Students' strategies for solving subtraction story problems will be assessed in the End-of-Unit Assessment, Session 3.8.

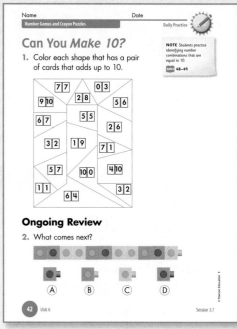

▲ **Student Activity Book, p. 42**

SESSION-FOLLOW-UP
Daily Practice

 Daily Practice: For reinforcement of this unit's content, have students complete *Student Activity Book* page 42.

 Student Math Handbook: Students and families may use *Student Math Handbook* pages 33–37 and G10, G11, G20 for reference and review. See pages 189–195 in the back of this unit.

End-of-Unit Assessment

Math Focus Points

◆ Solving addition and subtraction story problems

◆ Recording solutions to story problems

Today's Plan		Materials
ASSESSMENT ACTIVITY **1 End-of-Unit Assessment**	60 MIN INDIVIDUALS	• M55* • Cubes or counters (as needed)
SESSION FOLLOW-UP **2 Daily Practice**		• *Student Activity Book,* p. 43 • *Student Math Handbook,* pp. 33–37, 38–42

*See *Materials to Prepare,* p. 101.

Classroom Routines

Morning Meeting: Discussing the Yearly Data Follow your daily *Morning Meeting* Routine. During *Weather,* discuss the data that has been collected for the year. Choose a category and ask students to look at the data collected.

How many days has it been [rainy] so far this year? How do you know?

Have students share their strategies.

① End-of-Unit Assessment

60 MIN INDIVIDUALS

This end-of-unit assessment focuses on two of the unit's benchmarks.❶

Provide students with copies of the End-of-Unit Assessment (M55). Students work individually to solve two assessment problems that assess Benchmarks 3 (interpret and solve addition and subtraction story problems) and 4 (subtract one small quantity from another).

Explain that students will work individually to solve two story problems, so that you can get a sense of how they have grown in their ability to solve such problems and show their work.

Read aloud the story problems on End-of-Unit Assessment (M55).

Problem 1

Sam had 13 pencils. His friend gave him 4 more pencils. How many pencils did Sam have?

Problem 2

Kim had 15 balloons. She gave away 7 of them. How many balloons did she have left?

Remind students of the tools available to solve the problems. Remind them that they need to record in such a way that someone could tell how they solved the problem by looking at their work.

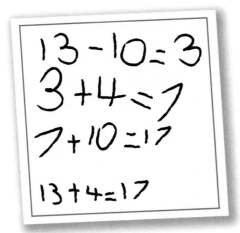

This student used number relationships he knew to solve an addition story problem.

Professional Development

❶ **Teacher Note:** End-of-Unit Assessment, p. 164

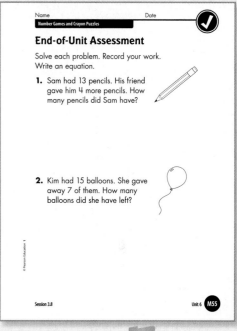

Name _____ Date _____
Number Games and Crayon Puzzles

End-of-Unit Assessment

Solve each problem. Record your work. Write an equation.

1. Sam had 13 pencils. His friend gave him 4 more pencils. How many pencils did Sam have?

2. Kim had 15 balloons. She gave away 7 of them. How many balloons did she have left?

Session 3.8   Unit 6 M55

▲ **Resource Masters, M55** PORTFOLIO

ONGOING ASSESSMENT: Observing Students at Work

After reading a story problem, students need to determine the action involved, and figure out whether they should add or subtract to solve the problem. Students then need to solve the problem and show their work.

At Grade 1, it is difficult to assess students solely from their written work as there is often a gap between their thinking and what they are able to put down on paper. Therefore, make a point to observe students as they work on these problems and jot down notes about how students approach the task. A combination of your observations and students' written work can give you a much fuller sense of students' strategies.

As you circulate, ask clarifying questions that will later help you remember how the student was thinking. Many teachers jot down a student's verbal explanation right on the Resource Master for later reference. In particular, look for explanations that do not tell you enough about what the student did (e.g., *"I counted"*). Ask questions such as:

- How did you count?

Jot down the student's response.

If you notice any mistakes, you may want to ask students to describe their strategy on the spot, and note whether articulating the process draws their attention to the error.

- **Can students make sense of the action in the problem?**

- **What tools and strategies do students use?**

- **Do students get the right answer?**

- **How do students record their work?**

Sample Student Work

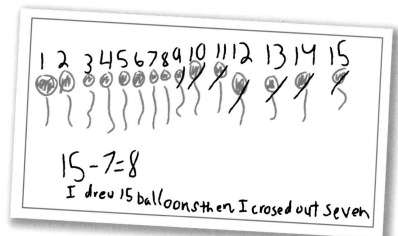

Sample Student Work

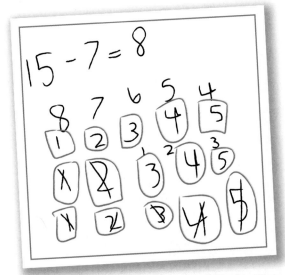

Sample Student Work

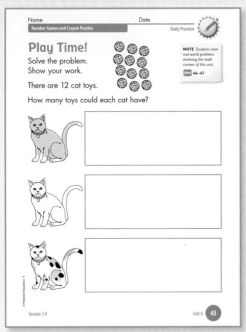

Student Activity Book, p. 43

2 Daily Practice

 Daily Practice: For enrichment, have students complete *Student Activity Book* page 43. This page provides real-world problems involving the math content of this unit.

Student Math Handbook: Students and families may use *Student Math Handbook* pages 33–37, 38–42 for reference and review. See pages 189–195 in the back of this unit.

Number Games and Crayon Puzzles

In Part 6 of *Implementing Investigations in Grade 1,* you will find a set of Teacher Notes that addresses topics and issues applicable to the curriculum as a whole rather than to specific curriculum units. They include the following:

Computational Fluency and Place Value

Computational Algorithms and Methods

Representations and Contexts for Mathematical Work

Foundations of Algebra in the Elementary Grades

Discussing Mathematical Ideas

Racial and Linguistic Diversity in the Classroom:
    What Does Equity Mean in Today's Math Classroom?

Using Notation

In *How Many of Each?* and *Solving Story Problems*, students were introduced to standard notation through teacher modeling, and many experimented with the use of such symbols. In this unit, the teacher continues to model the use of standard notation, but students are also explicitly asked to use standard notation to record their work in games like *Make 10*, *Tens Go Fish*, and *Dot Addition*.

Using Symbols

As students begin to use notation to record their work and show their strategies, there are some common issues to watch for.

Presented with an addition problem, students recorded in ways that show varying levels of understanding of standard notation.

I was cleaning the classroom. I found 5 pencils on the floor. I found 6 pencils by the window. How many pencils did I find?

Carol's Work

Chris's Work

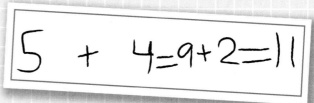

Tamika's Work

For students like Carol, it is a challenge to do more than use numbers to record their work. Others, like Chris, experiment with standard notation, but do not yet understand the meaning of the various symbols. Still others can communicate their strategy clearly, but misuse the symbols because of a misunderstanding of the equal sign. For example, it is clear that Tamika added 5 and 4 to get 9, and then added 2 to get 11. However, $5 + 4$ does *not* equal $9 + 2$, nor does it equal 11. This is why *Investigations* suggests that teachers record with separate equations. Ask students who record like this to consider whether $5 + 4$ in fact equals $9 + 2$. See **Teacher Note:** About the Equal Sign, page 141.

In the same classroom, students were asked to record solutions for the following subtraction problem.

Mrs. E. had 9 marbles. She gave 4 marbles to Sam. How many marbles did Mrs. E. have left?

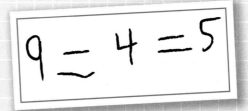

Jacinta's Work

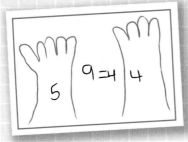

Paula's Work

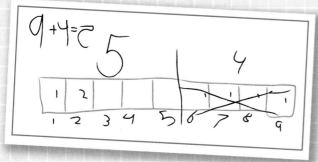

Seth's Work

As they attempt to use standard notation to record their work on subtraction problems, you are likely to see students who use = and + instead of −, as well as students who record the problem as $4 - 9 = 5$.

Such errors suggest that introducing standard notation to young children is not as simple as showing them the way to write an equation. The equation format may seem very straightforward to us as adults, but it actually assumes some complex ideas about number relationships. In Grade 1, many students are working to interpret problem situations and decide what actions are required to solve them. Students who are not making sense of the actions in problem situations should not be asked to use symbols to represent those actions. Those who *are* making sense of the actions are ready to grapple with how standard notation relates to those actions.

Although students are working more directly with notation in this unit, the emphasis for students must remain firmly on making sense of the problem situation and finding a way to solve it and record their work. First graders continue to work with standard notation and build on their experience with using it to represent addition and subtraction situations in Grade 2 and beyond.

Teacher Note

About the Equal Sign

As students begin to use standard notation to record their work, you are likely to see that some of them have misconceptions about the equal sign. Some students believe that this symbol means something like "now write the answer." Others use a run-on sentence style of recording, for example, writing "8 + 2 = 10 + 2 = 12" to show how they added 8 and 4. Still others think that equations must have an expression on the left side and a single number on the right: 6 + 10 = 16 or 14 − 7 = 7. Such misconceptions offer evidence that students are not seeing the equal sign as an indication of equality between what appears on either side. Consider the following vignette from a first-grade teacher.

After watching my students trying to use standard notation to record their work, I became curious about their understanding of the equal sign. I have been consciously trying to use the phrase, and help them come to understand the symbol to mean, "the same as." One day I wrote 3 = 2 + 1 on the board.

Keena: That's not right.

Teacher: What's not right?

Keena: The 3 does not go first.

Teacher: Where do you think it should be? What should I write instead?

Leah suggested writing *3 + 2 = 1* instead. I did, and the class was quick to comment that Leah's statement was not true—3 plus 2 did not equal 1.

Keena: 0 + 1 = 1, but not 3 + 2 = 1.

Richard: It should say 2 + 1 = 3.

The children agreed that this was the "right" way to write the equation, and that it was true—2 plus 1 did equal 3. We modeled the equation with cubes to prove it.

The discussion made me realize that students understood the equal sign to signal an answer. In other words, the equal sign separates "the problem to be solved" and "the answer." Moreover, the problem to be solved should be to the left of the equal sign and the answer must be to the right of the equal sign.

I decided to try a few more equations. The students had no trouble determining whether each equation was true or not when presented with a "simple" number sentence that they recognized (such as 1 + 3 = 4; 4 + 5 = 9; 7 + 8 = 15), and could use cubes to prove or disprove it.

However, the equation 4 = 4 caused some disagreement. We compared two cube towers of 4, and most students eventually agreed that 4 was the same as 4. I ended the discussion by asking students to reconsider the original problem: 3 = 2 + 1. The class was now divided. When asked to prove it right or wrong, they were able to use cubes to prove it correct. But most were still not comfortable with writing the "answer" first. I think that they will need more opportunities to explore the equal sign before they are secure that it means one side is the same as the other.

During class discussion this teacher discovers that her students are uncertain about the meaning of the equal sign.

Encouraging students to have such discussions will help them come to understand the equal sign as a "balance point"—whatever is on one side of the equation has to balance or be the same as whatever is on the other side. If one side equals 9, the other side also must equal 9.

When you use equations to record, be sure to use a variety of formats and to model them correctly. If a child adds $8 + 4$ by adding $8 + 2 + 2$ and writes $8 + 2 = 10 + 2 = 12$, use separate equations to model consecutive steps for the class.

$$8 + 4 = 8 + 2 + 2$$

$$8 + 2 = 10$$

$$10 + 2 = 12$$

Of course, what a first grader means by the string of expressions is clear: she added 8 and 2 first, and then added 2 to get 12. The child who writes this way simply understands the notation as a sequence of events, rather than as an equation. ($8 + 2$ is not equivalent to $10 + 2$.) Likewise, some first graders will not recognize that "order matters" when using subtraction notation. They might record $2 - 9$ to show that they took 2 away from 9. Encourage students to think about whether $2 - 9$ means the same thing as $9 - 2$.

Teacher Note

Strategies for Learning the Addition Combinations

To develop efficient computation strategies, students need to become fluent with the addition combinations from $1 + 1$ to $10 + 10$. Fluency means that combinations are quickly accessible mentally, either because they are immediately known or because the calculation that is used is so effortless as to be essentially automatic (in the way that some adults quickly derive one combination from another, for example, thinking $8 + 9 = 8 + 10 - 1$).

In *Investigations,* students will be fluent with all of the addition combinations to $10 + 10$ by the end of Grade 2. By the end of Grade 1, most students will be comfortable adding 1 or 2 to any number, and with many of the doubles. All students are expected to be fluent with the combinations that make 10 by the end of Grade 1.

Why Do We Call Them *Combinations*?

The addition problems from $1 + 1$ through $10 + 10$ are traditionally referred to as "addition facts"—those combinations with which students are expected to be fluent. Following the convention used by the National Council of Teachers of Mathematics (NCTM), the *Investigations* curriculum calls these expressions *combinations* rather than *facts. Investigations* does this for 2 reasons. First, naming *only* particular addition and multiplication combinations as *facts* seems to give them elevated status. Thus, they sound more important than other critical parts of mathematics.

In addition, the word *fact* implies that something cannot be learned through reasoning. For example, it is a fact that the first president of the United States was George Washington, and it is a fact that Rosa Parks was born in Alabama in 1913. If these facts are important for us to know, we can remember them or use reference materials to look them up. However, the sum of $7 + 8$ can be determined in many ways; it is logically connected to our system of numbers and operations. If we forget the sum, but understand what addition is and know some related combinations, we can

find the sum through reasoning. For example, if we know that $7 + 7 = 14$, then we can add 1 more to get 15. If we know that $8 + 8 = 16$, then we can take 1 away and get 15. If we know that $7 + 3 = 10$, we can then add the 5 that is left from the 8 to get 15. $(7 + 8 = 7 + 3 + 5 = 15)$

The term *facts* does convey a meaning that is generally understood by some students and family members, so you will need to decide whether to use the term *facts* along with *combinations* in certain settings in order to make your meaning clear.

Learning the Addition Combinations Fluently

The *Investigations* curriculum, like NCTM, supports the importance of students learning the basic combinations fluently through a focus on reasoning about number relationships: "Fluency with whole-number computation depends, in large part, on fluency with basic number combinations—the single digit addition and multiplication pairs and their counterparts for subtraction and division. Fluency with basic number combinations develops from well-understood meanings for the four operations and from a focus on thinking strategies . . ." (*Principles and Standards for School Mathematics, pp. 152–153*)

In other words, students learn these combinations best by using strategies, not simply by rote memorization. Relying on memory alone is not sufficient, as many of us know from our own schooling. If you forget—as we all do at times—you are left with nothing. If, on the other hand, your learning is based on an understanding of numbers and their relationships, you have a way to rethink and restructure your knowledge.

Through the number work in Grade 1, many first graders begin to use several important strategies as they think about addition combinations. When you see students using such strategies, encourage them to articulate and build on this thinking, and to share it with their classmates.

- **Adding 1s and 2s** Adding 1 or 2 easily is a beginning step in learning addition combinations. Students begin to "just know" that any time you add 1 to a number, you end up with the next number in the counting sequence. After students have had many experiences adding on 1 object to a group of objects, they are able to coordinate the idea of adding on 1 with their knowledge of the counting numbers. Building on this idea, they begin to add on 2 by quickly counting on two more numbers.

$$3 + 1 = 4$$
$$3 + 2 = 5$$

"I count on 1 more to 4, and two more to 5."

- **Doubles** Students learn many of the doubles (3 + 3, 4 + 4, 5 + 5, and so forth) quite early. Some students can begin to use the doubles they know to help them figure out other combinations.

$$5 + 5 = 10$$
$$6 + 5 = 11$$

"I know that 5 + 5 is 10, so 6 + 5 is 11."

- **Combinations that make 10** Fluency with these combinations, a focus of Unit 1 and Unit 3, is expected by the end of Grade 1. Some students will even build on these combinations to find others.

$$6 + 4 = 10$$
$$6 + 5 = 11$$

"I know that 6 + 4 is 10, so 6 + 5 is 11."

Since fluency develops through frequent and repeated use, students play games and engage in activities that focus on those combinations. For example, students:

- Play *Make 10, Counters in a Cup, How Many Am I Hiding?,* and *Tens Go Fish*

- Solve related story problems about 10

- Participate in activities like *Quick Images* and *Today's Number* that focus on the number 10

Students are expected to be fluent with the combinations of 10 by the end of Grade 1. Most will be comfortable with combinations that involve + 1 and + 2, and will also know quite a few other combinations, including doubles. Some students will not yet be able to use the combinations they know to find other combinations, but many will. Your students will have many opportunities to continue work on number combinations in Grade 2.

About How Many of Each? Problems in This Unit

Students have worked with How Many of Each Problems in Unit 1 and Unit 3. The focus of the *How Many of Each?* work in this unit is on finding *all* the solutions for a given context (or as many as students can find), and on thinking about whether all of the solutions have been found.

Students are asked to *prove* that they have found all the solutions and to explain *how they know*. Note that not all first graders will be able to find and prove that they have found all the possible 2-addend combinations of a given number. Yet, all students are challenged in this way because it encourages them to find relationships among solutions and to think and work more systematically. While the examples in this Teacher Note are from previous units, each one is used because it is representative of students' attempts to find all the solutions.

By the end of Unit 3, most students can find several solutions to a How Many of Each? problem. However, many students work almost randomly, not noticing relationships among solutions and not using one solution to find another. Although they keep a record of their work, many students do not notice when they arrive at the same solution more than once. Some may even tell you that they have found all possible solutions—not because they have ways to check, but because they have so many solutions that they think there could not possibly be more.

Using One Solution to Find Another

The challenge of finding as many 2-addend combinations of a number as possible often moves students into thinking about whether the solutions they have found provide clues for finding others. For example, as they look for more combinations, some students discover that if 8 marbles and 1 block is a solution, so is 1 marble and 8 blocks; if 4 marbles and 5 blocks is a solution, so is 5 marbles and 4 blocks. By reversing the numbers in one solution, they find a second.

Another way students derive new combinations is to take one marble in a solution they have and turn it into one block. That is, if 8 marbles and 1 block is a solution, then so is 7 marbles and 2 blocks. They can also take one block and make it one marble. If 2 marbles and 7 blocks is a solution, so is 3 marbles and 6 blocks. See **Teacher Note: Finding Relationships among Solutions, Unit 3, page 179,** for more information.

Showing You Have Them All

For many students, figuring out whether they have all of the possible combinations requires finding a systematic way of recording or showing solutions, a way that will "catch" all possibilities. In one class, a child presented the following cube structure to show that she had found all of the possible combinations of 9 blocks and marbles.

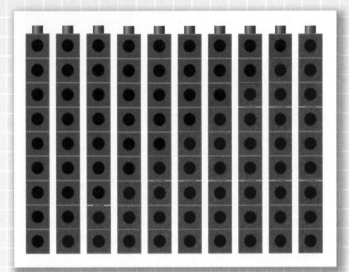

Emilia's Work

Each column represents 1 solution. The first is 0 blocks and 9 marbles; the next is 1 block and 8 marbles; the next is 2 blocks and 7 marbles; up to 9 blocks and 0 marbles. It is impossible to have any more than 9 blocks or 9 marbles, and all the possibilities less than 9 are included.

Other students may organize this information in a list or attempt to describe their process. Consider these examples of student work for a How Many of Each? problem about 11 apples and bananas.

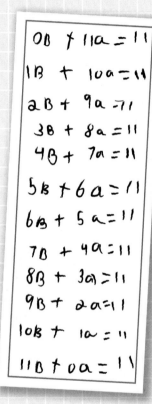

Felipe's Work

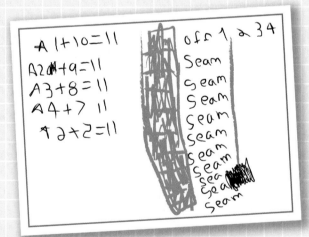

Tamika's Work

Tamika says, "Take 1 off, then 2, then 3 and keep doing the same ("seam")." The explanation that underlies all of the student work is the same: You cannot go higher than 11, and all possible values less than 11 are included.

Extending How Many of Each? Problems Students are also introduced to variations of How Many of Each? problems called Crayon Puzzles. These puzzles contain an additional piece of information—which set has more. See **Teacher Note:** About Crayon Puzzles, page 147, for more information.

About Crayon Puzzles

After revisiting a How Many of Each? problem in its familiar form, students are introduced to variations called Crayon Puzzles. Crayon Puzzles are more challenging than How Many of Each? problems because they contain another clue—the relative size of each set—which introduces an additional condition that students' answers must meet. All students solve Crayons Puzzles in which there are *more* of one color than another.

I have 7 crayons. Some are blue and some are red. I have more blue crayons. How many of each could I have?

Leah wrote:

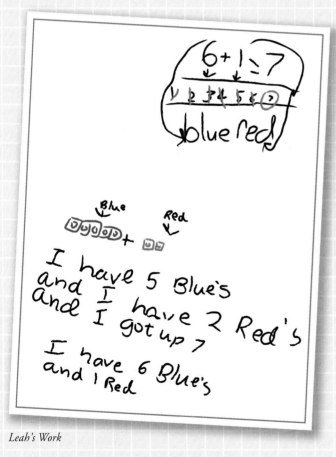

Leah's Work

First-grade students differ widely in how readily they can solve these puzzles. Many find it quite challenging to incorporate and keep track of an additional piece of information. Solving and discussing several Crayon Puzzles about *more* is enough of a challenge for them.

You may also have a group of students who enjoy the challenge of these puzzles and become excited about and engaged with them. Challenging Crayon Puzzles (M31–M36) are included precisely for these students. The challenging puzzles include puzzles about:

- Fewer
  I have 9 crayons.
  Some are blue and some are red.
  I have fewer blue crayons.
  How many of each could I have?

$$4 \text{ blues} + 5 \text{ reds} = 9$$
$$3 \text{ blues} + 6 \text{ reds} = 9$$
$$2 \text{ blues} + 7 \text{ reds} = 9$$
$$1 \text{ blue} + 8 \text{ reds}$$

Teo's Work

- Most and fewest
  I have 8 crayons.
  Some are blue, some are red, and some are green.
  I have the most blue crayons.
  How many of each could I have?

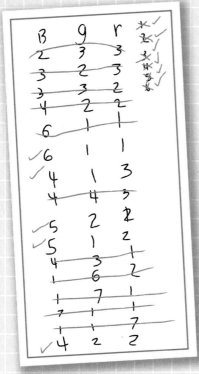

Deshawn's Work

- A combination of crayons that has *the same number* of red and blue crayons.
  I have 10 crayons.
  Some are blue and some are red.
  I have the same number *of each color.*
  How many crayons of each do I have?

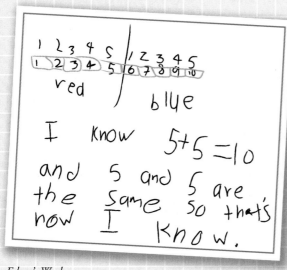

Edgar's Work

- A combination of crayons that has a given number of one color.
  I have 12 crayons.
  3 crayons are blue.
  The rest are red.
  How many crayons are red?

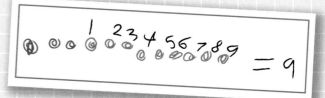

Bruce's Work

I have 10 crayons.
2 crayons are blue.
The rest are red.
How many crayons are red?

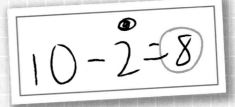

Neil's Work

These Crayon Puzzles can be offered as an additional Math Workshop activity, or during free times such as recess and before and after school. They can also be assigned as homework and can be used as models for creating additional puzzles.

Building on Number Combinations You Know

In Grade 1, most students are just becoming familiar with addition combinations from 0 + 0 to 10 + 10. As they work with numbers in many different ways, some first graders begin to reason about the combinations they already know to figure out others. During this Investigation, you may observe some of the following ways of thinking:

Counting On from a Known Combination

When playing *Dot Addition*, one student explained that she made 8 with 3 and 5 because "I know 3 and 3 is 6, and 2 more is 7, 8. But I didn't have enough 3s, so I put 2 and 3 together and made it 5." This approach is similar to counting on, a strategy that many students use for finding the total of 2 numbers. That is, to combine two numbers, they start at one and count on the other: "7 and 3 is— 8, 9, 10." Here, instead of beginning with a single number, the student began with a number combination, 3 + 3, and then she counted on 2 from the total (6) to reach the goal number (8). She then increased one of the addends in the combination accordingly: 3 + (3 + 2) = 3 + 5.

As students play Dot Addition, *they develop strategies for finding combinations of a given number.*

Counting Back from a Known Combination

One student used a counting back approach when he was playing *Counters in a Cup* with 15 counters. His partner had hidden some of the 15 counters in a cup, and 6 were showing outside the cup. This student reasoned that 9 were hidden because "10 plus 6 is 16, so take away 1 from 10 and it's 9, so 9 plus 6 is 15."

Your students will probably use counting back to find a new number combination only occasionally and only with very familiar combinations. Counting back and building numbers by "taking away" is less familiar to first graders than counting on and building numbers by combining parts.

Breaking a Familiar Combination into Parts and Recombining the Parts

One student made 15 in *Dot Addition* by beginning with a combination he knew, 8 + 7. To use the *Dot Addition* Cards, he needed numbers 5 or less, so he broke 8 into 5 and 3, and 7 into 5 and 2: 5 + 3 + 5 + 2. He checked his work by recombining the addends so that he could use combinations he knew: 5 and 5 is 10, 3 and 2 is 5, and 10 and 5 is 15.

This student recognized that the total remains the same, regardless of how the addends are broken into parts and regardless of the order in which the addends are combined. This flexible way of thinking about numbers is very powerful. When he combined the two 5s to make 10, and the 2 and 3 to make 5, he decided how to group the addends in the problem to make it easier to solve. He did not simply combine addends in the order in which they appeared. Note that he also used 10 as a familiar "landing place" in his calculation. He found a way to combine the addends to make 10 and then constructed a sum in which 10 is an addend. In the next year or two, as students gain more experience with 2-digit numbers, they will continue to develop strategies involving 10s and 1s.

Adjusting the Numbers in a Familiar Combination

Some first graders begin to recognize that if they add an amount to one addend in a number combination and take away the same amount from another, the total remains the same.

One student was solving a How Many of Each? problem for 12. He explained that he approached this problem by recording the first combination of 12 that came to mind,

$6 + 6$. He then decided to add 1 to the first 6 and take away 1 from the other 6, resulting in a new combination, $7 + 5$. He knew that the total would not change because "it's just adding 1 here and taking it away there; it's still 12."

To help your students think about building from number combinations they know, offer time for them to share strategies they have used in playing the games in this Investigation. However, avoid directly teaching these strategies. Although some students may begin this kind of reasoning with problems that involve smaller, more familiar numbers, they probably need many more experiences with number combinations over the next year or two before they will be able to use such strategies more broadly.

Assessment: Ten Crayons in All

Problem: Ten Crayons in All

Benchmark addressed:

Benchmark 1: Find at least five 2-addend combinations of 10.

In order to meet the benchmark, students' work should show that they can:

• Find and record at least five combinations of 10.

Most students find and record at least five combinations of 10; others find more than five, or even all of the possible combinations. Some students draw pictures while others use numbers, tables, and equations to record their work.

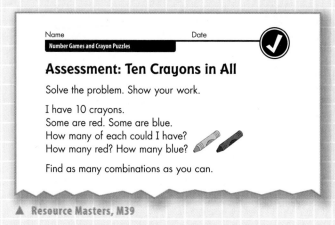

▲ Resource Masters, M39

Meeting the Benchmark

The following examples of student work provide a range of typical responses. All of these students meet the benchmark in that they were able to find at least 5 combinations of two addends that make 10 and record their work.

Consider sorting students' work for this problem twice. First, tally the total number of solutions found. Then, tally the total number of accurate solutions, not counting errors (e.g., 8 + 3) or repeated solutions.

Some students list combinations somewhat randomly. For example, it appears that Carol and Chris found and recorded one combination. Then they found and recorded another combination, which to them was unrelated.

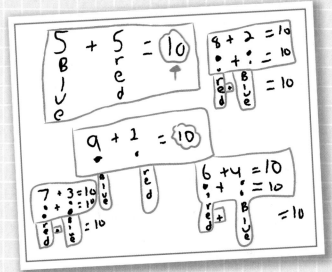

Carol's Work

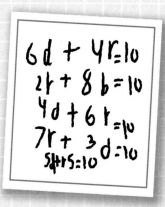

Chris's Work

On the other hand, Tamika and Libby seemed to work more systematically. For example, Tamika began with 5 + 5 and then created an ordered list that decreased the number of red crayons each time. Libby did something similar. After listing 5 + 5, she began with 1 red and 9 blue crayons and then increased the number of red crayons by 1 each time.

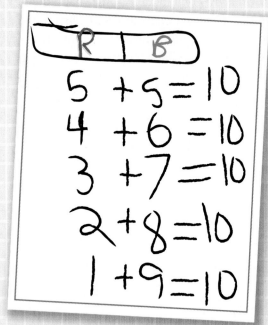

$$5 + 5 = 10$$
$$4 + 6 = 10$$
$$3 + 7 = 10$$
$$2 + 8 = 10$$
$$1 + 9 = 10$$

Tamika's Work

Some students will use "opposites" (Isabel) or strategies similar to those used by Tamika and Libby, to generate all of the combinations. Note how Vic explains how he knows he has all the possible combinations.

$$1 + 9 = 10 \qquad 9 + 1 = 10$$
$$2 + 8 = 10 \qquad 8 + 2 = 10$$
$$3 + 7 = 10 \qquad 7 + 3 = 10$$
$$4 + 6 = 10 \qquad 6 + 4 = 10$$
$$5 + 5 = 10 \qquad 5 + 5 = 10$$

Isabel's Work

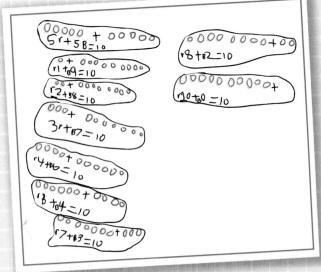

Libby's Work

b | r
$$9 + 1 = 10$$
$$8 + 2 = 10$$
$$7 + 3 = 10$$
$$6 + 4 = 10$$
$$5 + 5 = 10$$
$$4 + 6 = 10$$
$$3 + 7 = 10$$
$$2 + 8 = 10$$
$$1 + 9 = 10$$

I went in a patern

It works cause you only switch one so it HAS to work

$$9 + 1$$
$$8 \quad 2$$
$$7 \quad 3$$

Vic's Work

Not Meeting the Benchmark

You may find that some students add $10 + 10$ or list combinations of more than 2 addends, after their experience with Today's Number. However, at this point in the year, most students should understand the structure of this type of problem. Therefore, the majority of students who do not meet the benchmark will be those who are unable to find at least 5 accurate combinations of 10.

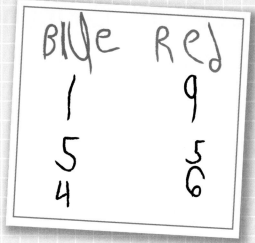

Danielle's Work

William's Work

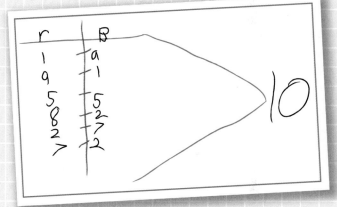

Nicky's Work

Student dictation: Those are all the ways I can think of.

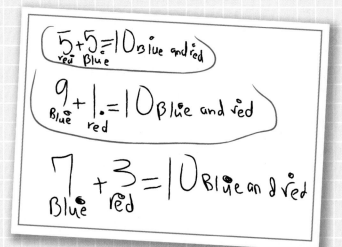

Toshi's Work

These students may need more time to work to find at least 5 combinations of 10. They will also benefit from further experience with How Many of Each? problems, and conversations about strategies for finding many combinations of a number, as in Session 2.1 of this unit. An extra How Many of Each? problem is provided on *Student Activity Book* page 16 (Nine Shapes: How Many of Each?), and you can use this as a model for developing others for further practice. Note whether students have more success when working with a smaller total.

Assessment: Counting On

By the end of this unit, students are expected to be adding two small numbers by at least counting on (Benchmark 2). Students are likely to fall into three groups:

Students Who Consistently Count On

These students consistently count on to add two numbers. For example, to add 8 and 3 these students say, *"8, 9, 10, 11."* Most first graders should be in this category at this point in the year.

Note that, in addition to counting on, some students may use more sophisticated strategies, such as using known combinations to solve problems that they do not know (e.g., *"I know 6 + 6 is 12, so 6 + 7 is 13."*). Also, a few students may "just know" some or many of these combinations. Keep track of this information in the far right column of Assessment Checklist: *Counting On* (M48).

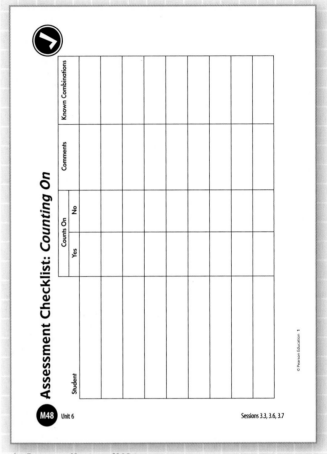

▲ Resource Masters, M48

Students Who Are Inconsistent

Some students count on to solve some problems, but count all to solve others. Note which combinations students solve with which strategy on your assessment checklist (M48).

Continued practice with 1 or several of the activities described below will help these students count on more consistently.

Students Who Are Not Yet Counting On

These students need to count each of the items on both of the Primary Number Cards in order to add the numbers.

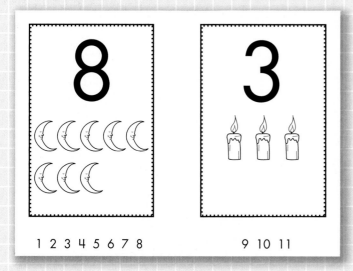

These students need more intensive practice with many or all of the activities described below.

Helping Students Count On Consistently

Students in the second and third categories described above need more practice with games and activities that encourage counting on. Many games (e.g., *Three Towers, Roll and Record, Five-in-a-Row*) can be modified to focus on counting on. Ask students to play with 1 number cube and 1 dot cube. *Student Activity Book* page 11 (Addition Problems) provides practice, and a model for making additional Practice Pages for students who need it. These can be done during free time at school or for homework.

Typically, students who are on the verge of counting on successfully struggle with where to start and stop counting, how many to count, and where to find the answer. This is particularly common when students are trying to count on in their heads, on their fingers, or on the number line or 100 chart. You can help students grapple with these issues by holding periodic discussions about counting on with these students. Once students can model the action of counting on with cubes or counters, you can focus on helping them connect the process of counting on with cubes to the process of counting on with one's fingers, the number line, and the 100 chart.

Note that sometimes students who count on consistently to combine 2 small numbers in a game format revert to counting all when solving story problems. Sometimes these students count on to solve the problem but find counting all easier to show on paper. Some students find the context and specificity of the story problems so central that they need to show more detail in their solutions, resulting in a paper that shows counting all. For other students, the attention they need to pay to other aspects of such a problem—reading the story, thinking about the sequence and action, modeling it, finding a way to record—result in their counting all for a problem they would count on for, if given a problem without a context (e.g., 8 + 7).

Three Approaches to Story Problems

Students commonly take one of these three approaches to solving an addition or subtraction story problem:

- Counting All

- Counting On (or Up) or Back (or Down)

- Numerical Reasoning

Each approach is described below and illustrated with examples of student work on the following problem. (Subtraction story problems are presented in Investigations 2 and 3.)

Last night I picked up 12 pencils from the floor. I put 4 of the pencils in the pencil box. How many pencils did I have left in my hand?

Counting All

When young students first encounter story problem situations, they usually model the actions in the problem step-by-step in order to solve it.

Students who are using a direct modeling strategy might count out 12 cubes, take 4 of them away to represent the 4 that were put in the pencil box, and then count the number of cubes remaining.

Leah drew 12 pencils, crossed out 4, and then counted the remaining pencils.

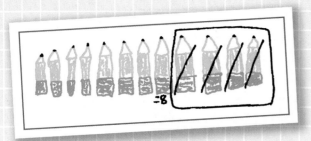

Leah's Work

Edgar counted out 12 cubes, took away 4, and counted the remaining cubes.

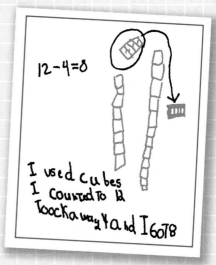

Edgar's Work

As students gain skill in visualizing problem situations and begin to develop a repertoire of number relationships they know, they gradually develop other strategies based on counting on or counting back and on numerical reasoning. These strategies require visualizing all of the quantities of the problem and their relationships, and recognizing which quantities are known and which need to be found.

Counting On or Counting Back

Some students, who perhaps feel more confident visualizing the problem mentally, use strategies that involve counting on or counting back.

Deshawn counted on his fingers. To get 12, he explained that he used both hands and visualized 2 "imaginary fingers." He counted back from 12, first counting back 2 in his head, using his imaginary fingers and then counting back 2 more on his actual fingers to get 8.

Deshawn recorded his counting back strategy on paper.

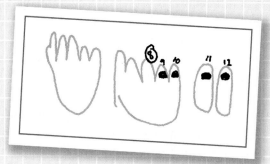

Deshawn's Work

Nicky used the class number line. She started at 12 and counted back 4.

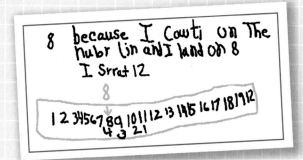

Nicky's Work

Bruce counted back 4 from 12 in his head.

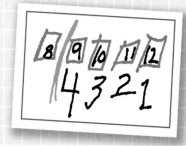

Bruce's Work

Although these three students' methods somewhat resemble the methods of the students who directly modeled the action in the problem, there is an important difference: None of these students had to construct the 12 from the beginning by 1s. Deshawn quickly made the 12 out of larger chunks (5 + 5 + 2), and Nicky and Bruce simply

started with 12. Counting back for subtraction requires a complex double counting method. These students must simultaneously keep track of the numbers they are counting back (11, 10, 9, 8) and the number of numbers counted (1, 2, 3, 4).

Isabel used a different counting strategy. She counted out 4 cubes in a column to represent the 4 pencils taken away. She continued putting cubes in a second column, counting on from 4 until she had a total of 12. Then she counted the number of cubes in the second column. Isabel was able to transform the problem into a different structure: $4 + \underline{\hspace{1cm}} = 12$, counting on to find the solution. See **Teacher Note:** The Relationship Between Addition and Subtraction, page 163, for more information.

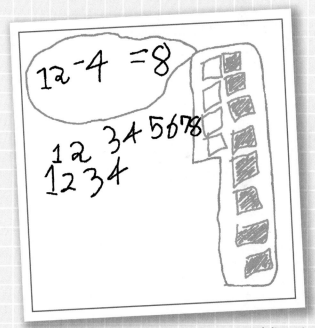

Isabel's Work

Using Numerical Reasoning

As students learn more about number relationships, they begin to be able to solve problems by taking numbers apart into useful chunks, manipulating those chunks, and then putting them back together.

Lyle broke 4 into 2 and 2. He then subtracted each chunk separately: 12 − 2 is 10, and then 10 − 2 is 8.

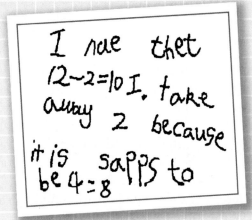

Lyle's Work

Tamika explained, "I know 4 and 4 and 4 is 12. Two 4s is 8, and then there's 4 in the pencil box."

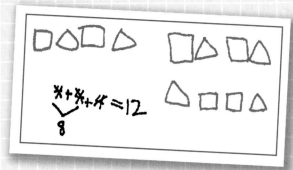

Tamika's Work

These students are using strategies that involve chunking numbers in different ways, rather than counting by 1s. They are able to visualize the structure of the problem as a whole in order to identify number relationships they know that might help them solve the problem. It is important to encourage strategies such as these, but keep in mind that ability to work with chunks greater than 1 develops gradually over the early elementary years. Many first graders will need to continue counting by 1s for most problems. As they build their understanding of number combinations and number relationships over the next year or two, as well as their ability to visualize the structure of a problem as a whole, they will begin to develop more flexible strategies.

Supporting Students as They Solve Story Problems

Some students will initially struggle to solve story problems on their own. To help these students, first try to find out what the source of the difficulty is. If students seem to be solving the problems by randomly doing something with the numbers, reread the story and ask them to tell the story in their own words. A next step might be to ask students to model the situation with counters or objects.

Diego and Jacob are working together on this problem:

Rosa had 15 pennies. She spent 5 pennies. How many pennies did she have left?

The teacher notices many tick marks and the numbers 5, 10, and 15 on their paper. When asked to explain their work, Diego and Jacob cannot. They have no trouble reading the problem, but are confused about where the 5 pennies come into play. She suggests that they try to model the problem with tiles. Jacob gets the tiles and tells Diego to pretend that they are pennies. Diego counts out 15 and Jacob takes 5 away. They count the remaining tiles and explain that these are the 10 pennies Rosa has left.

Teo is working with his teacher on this story problem:

Kim saw 20 ducks on the pond. Then 9 ducks flew away. How many ducks were still on the pond?

Teo notices the numbers 20 and 9 and tries to solve the problem without really understanding what is happening in the story. His teacher reads the problem aloud and has him retell the story with tiles. Teo counts out 20 tiles and takes away 9, removing a tile for each number. He counts the remaining tiles, touching each tile as he counts it. Then he draws 11 squares and writes "11."

Vic and Tamika are working on this problem:

Max picked 12 apples. He gave 6 of them to Rosa. How many apples did Max have then?

Vic has started his solution by drawing 12 apples, but now seems stumped.

Vic's Work

Vic rereads the problem with his teacher and then puts his hand after the sixth apple, creating a boundary between the sixth and seventh apples. He counts the apples to the right of his hand (numbered 7 through 12) and says, "6!" He smiles and writes 6 above his line of apples.

Tamika has asked her teacher for help.

Teacher: Tell me what happens in the story.

Tamika: Max gave Rosa 6.

Teacher: How many did he start with?

Tamika: 12.

Teacher: So what are you trying to figure out? Why don't we read the problem again? [They do.]

Tamika: I'm trying to figure out how many there's left. I'm trying to use my fingers but it's kind of tricky.

Teacher: Why is it tricky?

Tamika: Because I don't have 12 fingers.

Teacher: Is there something else you could use?

Tamika: My elbows.

Teacher: It might be a little tricky to count your fingers and your elbows. How about if I loan you some of my fingers. How many do you need?

Marta is working on this problem:

Rosa has 6 toy cars. Max gave her 4 more. How many cars did Rosa have then?

Marta wrote, "Rosa has 4. I took 10 tiles then I took 6 tiles then there was 4 tiles left." As the teacher rereads the problem aloud, Marta builds 2 towers, each 3 cubes tall. She explains that one is Rosa and the other is Max. She holds up each one in turn when the teacher mentions the names in the story. As the story continues, Marta builds and places a tower of 4 in front of "Max," and a tower of 6 in front of "Rosa." The teacher now asks Marta whether she can retell the story. She does, acting it out with the towers as she tells it. She ends the story with Rosa having all 10 cubes, and then she sets to work changing her paper.

Some students will quickly solve story problems. The challenge for teachers is knowing whether the given problems are the right level of difficulty. How does one know when to use the challenge problems? A good rule of thumb is to watch how students are solving the problems. The goal is for students to develop efficient and accurate ways to compute. If students are counting by 1s, the problems are not too easy for them.

Children like those described below, who consistently use more sophisticated strategies to solve story problems, are often ready for more challenge.

Libby is trying to solve this problem:

Max picked 12 apples. He gave 6 of them to Rosa. How many apples did Max have then?

Libby wrote "6 + 6 = 12 Take away 6 = 6". She could explain to her teacher how knowing 6 + 6 helped her solve 12 − 6.

William is working on this problem:

Yesterday I gave Lele, our class frog, 4 bugs to eat. Allie gave Lele 6 more bugs. How many bugs did Lele get?

William wrote this on his paper:

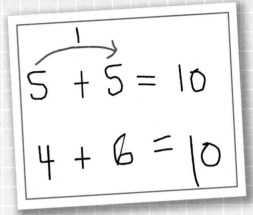

William's Work

When asked how he knew the answer was still 10, he said, "Because 5 + 5 = 10, so if you just take 1 more and 1 less it's still 10; 6 + 4 = 10."

Jacinta is trying to solve this problem:

Jake and Louisa were playing with the Geoblocks. Jake had 4 blocks. Louisa had 5 blocks. They worked together to make a building with all the blocks. How many blocks did they use?

Jacinta: I took 1 away from 10 and I got 9, I just knew it.

Teacher: How did you know 10?

Jacinta: 10 minus 1 is 9, so then between the 9 there's a 4 and a 5.

Supporting Students as They Record Story Problem Work

From the beginning, *Investigations* students are asked to show their work—to use numbers, pictures, words, and, if they are ready, equations to show how they solved a problem. Someone else looking at a student's paper should be able to understand how the student solved the problem.

For some students, showing anything on paper is difficult initially. Subtraction problems can be particularly challenging. How do you show that a group was removed or taken away on paper? Most often students use a combination of numbers, pictures, and words to record their work. As they learn more about standard notation, they will also use the various symbols and equations.

Words

Some students may write words such as "I counted" or "I knew it."

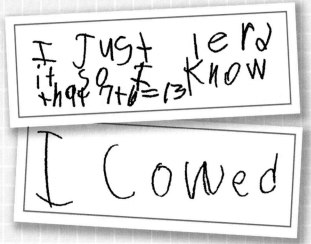

Encourage these students to explain *how* they counted. You might ask questions such as, "Where did you start counting? What numbers did you say when you counted?

Where did you stop? How did you know where to start/stop counting?" Then model how they might record their answers on paper.

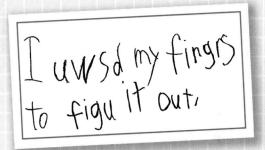

Pictures

Many students' first strategy is to show every item in the problem. For example, they will draw a group of 7 cars and a group of 6 cars in great detail. They may even include detailed drawings of the children in the story. One goal for this group of students is to help them attach numbers to their work. Although some students will have a hard time showing much more on paper than a picture of each individual car, you can ask how many cars are in each group, and then help the student label the groups.

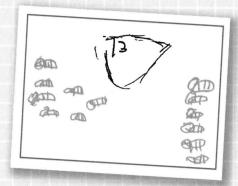

Sample Student Work

Another goal is to move these students toward more efficient methods of recording. Although some students will need to draw every single item, math papers can quickly become art projects. Discuss with students what is important to show in math (versus art) class. For some students, this might mean drawing cars with less detail. Others might use letters, pictures of cubes, or tallies to represent the cars.

Numbers and Equations

Another group of students will use only numbers (e.g., 7 6 13) or equations (e.g., $7 + 6 = 13$). It can be tricky to figure out how these students are solving the problem and to assess what they really understand about the notation they are using. Ask students who use only numbers, "I see these 3 numbers here. Can you tell me what they mean?" Help students add symbols where appropriate and find a way to show how they knew that 7 and 6 was 13. Ask students who use equations what their numbers and the symbols mean. You might take dictation when they explain (e.g., $6 + 6 = 12$ so $6 + 7 = 13$), or show students how to draw a heart next to a combination they "just know."

Sample Student Work

Recording the Strategy Used

Another challenge is helping students find a way to show the strategy they actually used, rather than one that is easy to show on paper. Many teachers say that this is common; they come across a student they know to be counting on, for example, to solve addition problems. The student's written work, however, suggests that she counted all. Ask these students to explain their strategy to you, and help them think about how they might show that. For example, students who count on their fingers can trace their hands and label the fingers they counted with the numbers said. You might also pair students who have solved the problem in similar ways or share a way you saw another child record something similar.

Many teachers say that they work with students on methods for recording from the beginning of the year. They model different methods of recording as they record for the whole class, individuals, or pairs. They ask students who have recorded differently to share their work with their classmates and may even pair up particular students purposefully. As the year proceeds, these teachers ask students to consider, "Does what I wrote up here show what Paula did?" They might occasionally record incorrectly on purpose. They sometimes ask one student to record another student's strategy or post a written strategy and ask how students think the person solved the problem. (See the **Dialogue Box:** Does This Show Paula's Strategy?, page 187, for some examples.)

The more that various models of recording are shared and discussed, the more options students will have as they decide how to show their thinking.

The Relationship Between Addition and Subtraction

Understanding the operations of addition and subtraction and gaining fluency in carrying out these operations are goals of much of the number work students do in the elementary grades. Understanding the relationship between addition and subtraction deepens students' understanding of the operations and ability to use them to solve problems.

As you introduce story problems to students, avoid labeling them as addition or subtraction. A critical skill in solving problems is deciding what operation is needed. Further, many problems can be solved in a variety of ways, and students need to choose an operation that makes sense to them for each situation.

It is easy for adults to assume that certain situations are addition and others subtraction because they are used to thinking of them that way. However, students may use addition to solve problems that you think of as subtraction. (In fact, many adults also do this.) Consider the following problem:

12 squirrels were on the ground. Then 4 of them ran up a tree. How many stayed on the ground?

Most of us learned to interpret this situation as subtraction, and we may naturally assume that students should also see it as subtraction. Students who use direct modeling of the actions to solve the problem will probably count out 12 objects, remove 4, and count how many remain. However, there are many other ways, such as the following, to solve this problem:

- Counting down 4 from 12 (11, 10, 9, 8)

- Counting on from 4 (5, 6, 7, 8, . . .) and keeping track of how many numbers are counted

- Using knowledge of number combinations and relationships ("I know 4 + 4 + 4 is 12, and two 4s is 8." or, "12 take away 2 is 10, so just take away 2 more; that's 8.")

Some of these methods are based on subtraction (moving from 12 down to 4), but others are based on addition (moving up from 4 to 12). The method chosen depends on a person's mental model of the situation. Do you see this problem as a taking-away situation to be solved by subtraction, as an adding-on situation, or as a gap between 2 numbers that might be solved by either addition or subtraction, depending on which is easier in the particular situation? Any of these methods is appropriate for solving this problem. Addition is just as appropriate for solving this problem as subtraction, and, for many students, makes more sense.

Sample Student Work

End-of-Unit Assessment

Problem 1

Benchmark addressed:

Benchmark 3: Interpret (retell the action and sequence) and solve addition and subtraction story problems.

In order to meet the benchmark, students' work should show that they can:

• Interpret an addition situation;

• Accurately combine 13 and 4;

• Show how they solved the problem.

To solve this problem, students might use the following strategies:

• Count all;

• Count on.

• Add the numbers by relying on combinations or relationships they know.

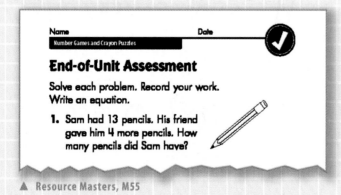

▲ Resource Masters, M55

Meeting the Benchmark

The following examples of student work provide a range of typical responses. All of these students meet the benchmark—they were able to interpret the problem and

solve it accurately. Note that students who are counting on or are adding the numbers based on combinations they know, are working more efficiently than those who are counting all.

Counting all While some first graders will be counting on to add two smaller numbers, a substantial group may still count all to solve story problems, particularly with numbers of this size. They count out or draw a group of 13 and a group of 4, and then recount the combined group of 17. They use a combination of words, pictures, numbers, and equations to show what they did.

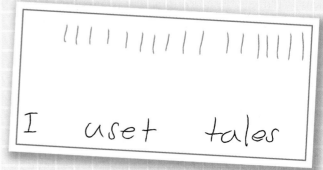

Carol's Work

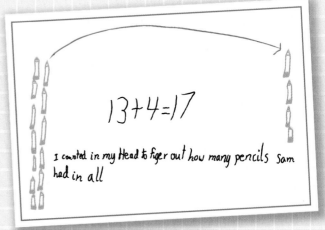

Chris's Work

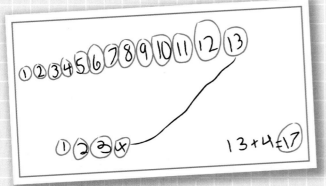

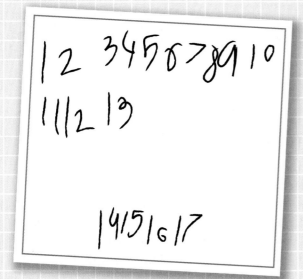

Tamika's Work

Counting on At this point in the year, particularly given that the problem involves adding a small amount (4) onto a larger number (13), more students will be counting on to solve this problem.

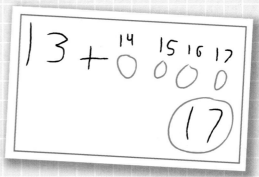

Isabel's Work

Libby's Work

Vic's Work

Note the variety of labels students choose to attach to their work. Some students show only a group of 17, with no clear subgroups of 13 and 4 (Carol), while others show 2 distinct groups (Chris). Some students do not label the groups in any way, while others label the totals of each group, each item in each group (Tamika), each item in the whole group (Libby), or each item in each group *and* the number in the entire group.

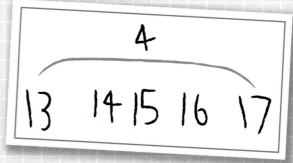

Lyle's Work

Although Felipe showed the entire number line, from 1, he used it to show how he counted on to solve the problem. When asked about his strategy he explained, "I used the number line. I started at 13 and went 14, 15, 16, 17."

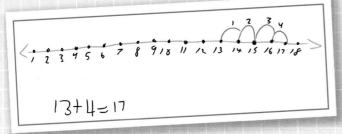

$$13 + 4 = 17$$

Felipe's Work

Adding Some students may use something they know to add the two numbers. For example, some students break 13 into $10 + 3$ and then solve $(3 + 4) + 10$. Others think, "If $3 + 4 = 7$, then $13 + 4 = 17$."

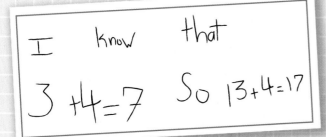

Marta's Work

I know that $3 + 4 = 7$ So $13 + 4 = 17$

Talisa's Work

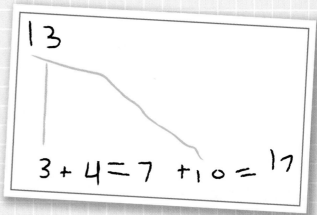

Paul's Work

Note that, although students like Paul are not accurately using standard notation, their thinking is quite sophisticated. With experience and time, these students will learn how standard notation can show such strategies.

Partially Meeting the Benchmark

Some students understand the structure of the problem—that it is about combining 2 quantities and finding the total number—but make mistakes as they count or recount the quantities in the problem. After you review their assessment, ask these students to double-check their work (e.g., "Your paper says that 13 plus 4 is 18. How could you double-check that?"). See whether they can find and correct such errors on their own. Encourage these students to take their time and work carefully to avoid such errors in the future. In addition, note whether these kinds of errors are consistent across problems or are more of a one-time occurrence.

Diego's Work

Other students understand the structure of the problem but struggle with knowing where to start and stop when counting on. These students may be losing the connection between the numbers and the situation, and may benefit from conversations that model counting on with cubes. For example, if there are already 13 cubes in one pile, then it makes sense to start counting on with 14, because 13 plus one more would be 14 (plus 2 more would be 15, etc.). Once they can model counting on clearly with cubes, they can compare and connect it to the process of counting on with their fingers, the number line, or the 100 chart.

Not Meeting the Benchmark

Some students may still be constructing an understanding of the structure of the problem. For example, when asked what her answer was, Keena recounted her pencils and said, "16." His teacher then reread the problem and asked her to double-check her work. She recounted all of the pencils and once again said, "16." It took further conversation with her teacher, about the size of the two groups, to find and correct this error. At this point in the year, Keena's grasp of problems of this type does not meet the benchmark.

Keena's Work

Students in this category likely need more experience counting quantities by 1s, and directly modeling the action of such problems with cubes. *Student Activity Book* pages 5 and 27 (and others modeled after them) provide more practice with addition story problems.

Problem 2

Benchmarks addressed:

Benchmark 3: Interpret (retell the action and sequence) and solve addition and subtraction story problems.

Benchmark 4: Subtract one small quantity from another.

In order to meet the benchmarks, students' work should show that they can:

- Interpret a subtraction situation about removal;

- Accurately subtract one quantity from another;

- Show how they solved the problem.

To solve this problem students might use the following strategies:

- Count all.

- Count back or up.

- Subtract by relying on combinations or relationships they know.

2. Kim had 15 balloons. She gave away 7 of them. How many balloons did she have left?

▲ **Resource Masters, M55**

Meeting the Benchmarks

The following examples of student work provide a range of typical responses. All of these students meet the benchmark in that they were able to interpret the problem and solve it accurately. However, students who are counting back or using combinations or relationships they know to subtract are demonstrating a deeper understanding of the operation of subtraction and of the quantities in the problem than those who are counting all.

Counting all Many first graders count all to solve this problem—they draw 15, cross out (or circle or separate) 7, and count how many are left. They use a combination of words, pictures, numbers, and equations to show their work.

Carol's Work

Note that some students attach no labels to their work (Carol), while others label each item in the initial group (Chris), the total in each group (Tamika), each item in the remaining group (Libby), or each item in the whole group and in the subgroups.

Counting back or down A few students may count back to solve this problem, on their fingers, on the number line (Teo), or in their heads. Some students draw pictures of the tools they used (number line, fingers), while others write the numbers they said.

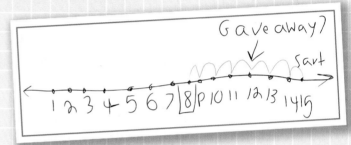

Teo's Work

Counting up Some students count up from 7 to 15, to find the distance between the two numbers. At first glance, Vic's teacher thought he had counted back. However, when Vic demonstrated *how* he counted on his fingers, he counted up from 7 to 15. His teacher added the words "from 7" to his paper, for her reference.

Chris's Work

Tamika's Work

Vic's Work

Libby's Work

Numerical strategies A few first graders use something they know to solve 15 − 7. Lyle and Felipe both know that 15 − 5 = 10. Lyle then counts back "9, 8" to subtract 2 more. Felipe uses a pattern using 15 − 5 to figure out 15 − 6 and 15 − 7.

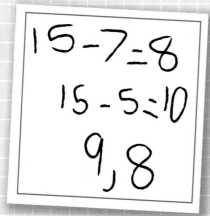

Lyle's Work

Felipe's Work

To solve 15 − 7, Paul thinks of an addition combination he knows, 7 + 7. He then uses the relationship between addition and subtraction, thinking, "if 7 + 7 = 14 then 7 + 8 = 15, and if 7 + 8 = 15 then 15 − 8 = 7."

Paul's Work

Partially Meeting the Benchmarks

Some students understand the structure of the problem, that it is about removing one quantity from another and then finding out how many are left, but make small computational or keeping track mistakes. For example, when counting all it is easy to miscount the total number (Marta and Talisa), the number taken away (Diego), or the number remaining.

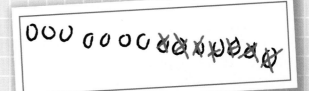

Marta's Work

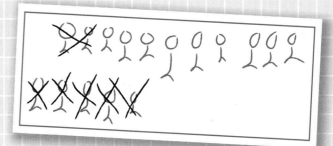

Talisa's Work

Diego's Work

After you review their assessment, ask these students to double-check their work (e.g., "Your paper says that 15 minus 7 is 9. How could you double-check that?"). See whether they can find and correct such errors on their own.

Encourage these students to take their time and work carefully to avoid such errors in the future. In addition, note whether these kinds of errors are consistent across problems or more of a one-time occurrence.

Other students understand the structure of the problem but struggle with knowing where to start and stop when counting back or up. These students may be losing the connection between the numbers and the situation, and may benefit from conversations that model these strategies with cubes. For example, if there are already 15 cubes in a pile, then it makes sense to start counting back with 14, because 15 minus 1 is 14. (Or, "Here are 7 balloons. How many more do we need to get to 15? If we add 1 more that's 8, another one is 9 . . . ") Once they can model these strategies with cubes, they can compare and connect them to the process of using their fingers, the number line, or the 100 chart.

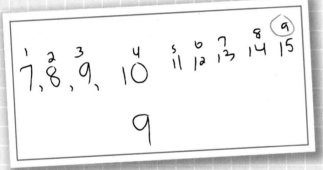

Keena's Work

Not Meeting the Benchmarks

Other students have difficulty interpreting and modeling a story that is not about combining or addition. It is not uncommon to see students show the two numbers in the problem, a group of 15 and a group of 7. Some do not know what to do next, know that crossing out seems to be important, or combine the two amounts.

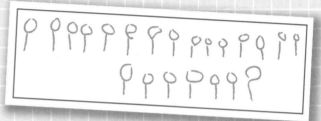

Allie's Work

Students in this category need more support making sense of what the problem is asking. They may benefit from practice retelling stories about subtraction, and directly modeling the action of such problems with cubes. They will also benefit from finishing the story problems in Investigations 2 and 3, if they have not already. Also, *Student Activity Book* page 38 (Solving a Story Problem) provides a subtraction story problem, and a model for making additional ones.

Pictures and Equations

During *Quick Images: Pictures of 10,* page 27, students are sharing their thinking about image A. The teacher sketches the image on the board and helps them find ways to use equations to describe how they broke the image into parts.

Teacher: What did you notice about the image? What helped you remember it?

Stacy: I saw lines of dots.

Teacher: How many?

Stacy: Two.

Jacob: There are 5 in each row.

The teacher circles each row of 5.

Teacher: So, two rows of 5 dots. How does that help us think about the total number of dots?

Jacob: You add them together.

Teacher: What numbers would you use?

Leah: Five plus 5.

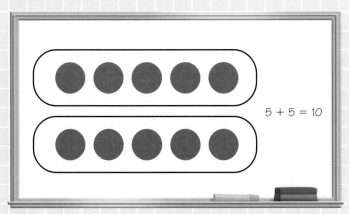

$$5 + 5 = 10$$

The teacher records $5 + 5 = 10$ to the right of the sketch.

Teacher: Five [points to the top row] and 5 [the bottom row] is 10 in all. Who thought about this picture in a different way?

Diego: I saw 2s. I counted by 2s.

Teacher: What did you say when you counted? Do you want to come up and show us?

Diego comes to the overhead and counts each "column" of two: 2, 4, 6, 8, 10. The teacher circles each corresponding column on the board.

Teacher: How could you write it?

Diego: Two plus 2 is 4. So, um . . . so, you write $2 + 2$ . . . That's 4, so write $+ 4$ . . . then $+ 6$?

Several students raise their hands eagerly, but the teacher motions for silence.

Teacher: OK, let's take this one step at a time. What's this one [points to the leftmost column]?

Diego: Two.

The teacher writes 2 above the column. And this next one [points to the next column]?

Diego: Um . . . plus 2.

The teacher writes $+ 2$.

Teacher: And?

Diego: Two plus 2 . . . oh, plus 2 . . . plus 2 plus 2. Plus 2 for each of those.

The teacher writes in the remaining $+ 2$s.

Teacher: OK, so, that's 2 + 2 + 2 + 2 + 2.
And it equals?

Bruce: [Counting off each 2 on a finger]: 2, 4, 6, 8, 10.
Five sets of 2 equals 10.

$$2 + 2 + 2 + 2 + 2 = 10$$

The teacher writes = 10 at the end of the expression.

Teacher: OK, five 2s equals 10. Is there another way?

Tamika: One plus 1 plus 1 plus 1 plus 1 plus 1 plus . . .
Wait. How many ones did I say?

Teacher: How many 1s are there in the picture?
How many 1s should there be?

Tamika: One for each dot. Ten.

Teacher: So, what should we write?

As Tamika counts, keeping track on her fingers. the teacher
records each + 1 and then quickly draws a box around
each dot.

Teacher: Let's count the 1s to make sure that I have the
right number of them. [The class counts as the teacher
points to each 1.] So, each of those 1s stands for one of
the dots in the picture.

$$1 + 1 + 1 + 1 + 1 + 1 + 1 + 1 + 1 + 1 = 10$$

Dialogue Box

Today's Number: 10

This class is sharing combinations of 10 that they have found for the *Today's Number* activity (Session 1.1, page 28). The teacher records each suggestion on chart paper. As students compare the combinations in the growing list, they begin to think about the relationships among them.

Teacher: Who can give us one way you found to make 10?

Carol: 8 + 1 + 1.

Teacher: How do you know that's 10?

Carol: [Holds up 8 fingers] 8 and 1 [another finger] is 9, and 1 more [another finger] is 10.

Teacher: Who has another combination of 10?

William: 3 and 7. I thought of 7, and I counted up 8, 9, 10.

Felipe: 5 + 5.

Teacher: How do you know?

Felipe: Because 5 [holds up one hand] and 5 [holds up the other hand] is 10 in all.

Teo: I have another one: 5 + 4 + 1.

Teacher: How do you know that's 10?

Teo: 4 + 1 is 5. And it's like what Felipe did: 5 and 5.

Toshi: You can do it to both!

Teacher: Do what to both?

Toshi: Both 5s. They can both be 4 + 1.

Teacher: So, you can break up each 5 into 4 and 1, to get 4 + 1 + 4 + 1. Who has something else?

Lyle: 3 + 1 + 6.

Sacha: We already have it, in a way.

Teacher: Can you tell us what you mean?

Sacha: Its like 3 + 7, because 3 and 1 and 6 . . . You put the 1 in the 6. Then its the same.

Teacher: Sacha is saying they're similar—if you have 3 + 1 + 6 and you add up the 1 and the 6. You end up with 3 + 7.

Nicky: Here's one: 4 and 4 and 1 and 1.

Teacher: How do you know that's 10?

Nicky: I took the first one [the expression 8 + 1 + 1] and made it 4 and 4.

When the teacher adds 4 + 4 + 1 + 1 to the list, students call out that it is already there.

Teacher: We have 4 + 4 + 1 + 1, and 4 + 1 + 4 + 1. What do you think? Are they the same?

Edgar: They're the same numbers.

Nicky: My way is in a different order.

Teacher: The same numbers in a different order. They both have two 4s and two 1s. Toshi thought of 5 and 5, and he broke each 5 into 4 and 1. Nicky thought of it as 8 and 1 and 1, and broke the 8 into 4 and 4.

Isabel: I have a new way: 8 and 2.

Carol: We already have that. It's the first one.

Teacher: [Pointing to 8 + 1 + 1] I don't see a 2.

Carol: But 1 and 1 is 2. It's the same thing.

Isabel: I put the 1 + 1 together, so it looks like 8 + 1 + 1, but it isn't. They used three numbers to make 10, and I used two numbers because I put the 1 and 1 together.

Do We Have *All* of the Combinations?

The students in this class have had several experiences with How Many of Each? problems. Prior to this discussion, the class had been trying to find all of the ways to make 9 toys if some were marbles and some were blocks. The students generated a list of 10 possible combinations, but were unable to reach a consensus on whether this list represented all of the ways to make 9. The teacher decided to end the discussion and continue it today.

> 5 blocks + 4 marbles
>
> 2 marbles + 7 blocks
>
> 9 marbles + 0 blocks
>
> 3 marbles + 6 blocks
>
> 6 marbles + 3 blocks
>
> 8 marbles + 1 block
>
> 1 marble + 8 blocks
>
> 0 marbles + 9 blocks
>
> 5 marbles + 4 blocks
>
> 7 marbles + 2 blocks
>
> Today we found 10 ways. Is that all?

Teacher: The other day, we talked about finding all of the different ways to make 9. Here is the list that we came up with so far. While you were working on How Many of Each? problems, I saw Isabel use an interesting strategy, and I'm going to ask her to share it with everyone.

She gives Isabel a stick of 9 cubes to use for her demonstration. Isabel breaks one cube off.

Teacher: What does that show?

Isabel: 1 marble and 8 blocks.

The teacher records 1 marble + 8 blocks on a new piece of chart paper.

Teacher: How come you broke only 1 off?

Isabel: I don't know . . . because then you could go 2 [breaks off 2 cubes]. And then 3, and then 4, 5, 6, 7, 8.

Teacher: So you had a plan. You wanted to start with 1 on purpose. Who can tell us about Isabel's plan?

Marta: She thought she could go 1 and 8 so she could find all the ways and then 2 and 7.

Teacher: If Isabel's plan were to do 1 and 8 [breaks 1 cube off the tower of 9 to demonstrate], who can show me what our next answer would be?

Neil: 8 and 1.

Teacher: OK, I think you might be thinking of another strategy. Can you hold onto that idea until we finish talking about Isabel's strategy? [Neil agrees and the teacher reiterates Isabel's plan.] So what would be the next answer?

Neil: 2 and 7.

Teacher: And then what?

Paula: Um . . . 3 and 6.

Marta: We're counting up and down. Cool!

> 1 marble + 8 blocks
>
> 2 marbles + 7 blocks
>
> 3 marbles + 6 blocks

Teacher: How do you know that these are making 9?

Marta: Because there are 9 cubes.

Teacher: So, is there anything important about the tower of cubes we're using? Why did you want to make sure that there were 9 cubes?

Jacob: Well, it has to have a certain amount. It has to have 9.

Deshawn: [signals that he agrees] It has to have 9 for this problem, but other days we used different numbers so we would need a different size tower.

Stacy: I think I can prove that we have all the ways. [She uses green and yellow cubes to make the figure below on the floor in front of her.]

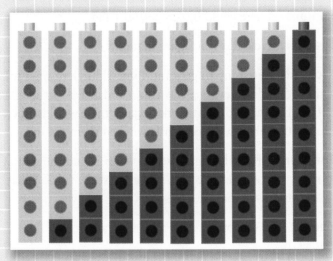

Diego: Look! It makes a ladder.

Vic: Oh, it's like a staircase!

Shaquana: I can see the opposites [holds up the 2nd and the 9th towers].

Teacher: How does that prove that that's all of the ways?

Stacy: Because I took away all of the ways. Because . . . I can't really explain it, but I know it is.

Teacher: OK, so maybe if you work a little more with it, you'll be able to explain. We have one other idea to talk about. Neil said he would do 8 and 1 next. So we would have 1 marble and 8 blocks and 8 marbles and 1 block. And then what would you do next?

Neil: 7 marbles and 2 blocks and 2 marbles and 7 blocks.

Teacher: And what would come next?

Paula: 6 marbles and 3 blocks and 3 marbles and 6 blocks.

Although many students are not yet able to work systematically to generate all the 2-addend combinations of a number, these students have discovered and discussed 2 ways that they might organize their work to think about whether they have all the possible combinations. Note that even after Stacy has built towers that she is sure show every combination, it is difficult for her to explain how they show that those are all of the ways. Understanding the structure of a problem or strategy often precedes being able to verbalize an explanation of it.

Introducing Crayon Puzzles

In the following vignette, a teacher introduces Crayon Puzzles (Session 2.2, page 77) to her students, after they have had a lot of experience with How Many of Each? problems. Note how she highlights what is known and unknown in order to help students make sense of Crayon Puzzles, and how they are different from How Many of Each? problems.

Teacher: Today we are going to work on something new called crayon puzzles. I'm going to give you an example of a crayon puzzle. Think about how we might solve this problem, or what might help us solve this problem.

[She reads the problem aloud, twice.] I have 5 crayons. Some are blue and some are red. There are more blue crayons than there are red crayons. How many of each can I have? . . . What do we need to find out?

Libby: We don't know how many reds and how many blues.

Paula: Aren't you supposed to try to figure out ways to make 5 with more blue crayons than red?

Teacher: So you discovered that there is an extra rule for this problem. What is the rule you found?

Paula: That it has to make 5 but there needs to be more blue than red.

Teacher: OK, so I'm going to make a list over here of what we know and what we don't know. What do we know for sure?

Edgar: We know that there are 5.

Teacher: OK, so we know that there are 5 crayons total.

Carol: There has to be more blue crayons than red.

Teacher: OK, so one rule is that there has to be 5 altogether and the other rule is that there are more blue than red. What are we trying to find out?

Jacob: How many of each?

Teacher: So we are trying to find out how many red and how many blue there are.

What We Know	What We Are Trying to Find Out
5 crayons total	How many of each?
More blue than red	How many red? How many blue?

Richard: There could be 4 blue and 1 red.

Teacher: How did you figure that out?

Richard: I used my fingers and I knew different ways to make 5 and I knew one way was 4 and 1. First I thought 4 red but that wouldn't work because there wouldn't be more blue than red. So then I switched them around.

Teacher: OK, so Richard used his fingers and thought of 4 and 1. Then he tested his idea against the rules. What is another way that we can solve this?

Keena: You can pretend the tiles are crayons.

Teacher: Keena, can you show us how you would use the color tiles to help you solve the problem?

Keena chooses 2 red and 3 blue tiles. She lines them up in 2 rows.

Teacher: Why did you line them up?

Keena: It made it easier to see it.

Teacher: See what?

Keena: That there's more blues.

Teacher: So when you are working on these puzzles today, what are some questions you should ask yourselves before you get started?

Jacob: What do you know?

Tamika: And what are you trying to find out?

1 Think There's Only 3 Ways

This teacher noticed that Emilia was using a powerful strategy to solve Crayon Puzzles. Hoping that such a strategy will help students see the advantage of working more systemically and organizing their work, she asks Emilia to share her strategy with the class.

Teacher: We are going to talk about puzzle number 3 today. Listen carefully: I have 7 crayons. Some are blue and some are red. I have more red crayons. How many of each could I have? When Emilia was solving this problem, she found a new way to think of it. Emilia, would you share your strategy with us?

Emilia agrees. She has a sheet of white paper, a red marker, a blue marker, and a black marker. First she writes 6 + 1 = 7 in black.

Teacher: What did she do first?

Neil: She wrote an equation. She wrote 6 + 1 = 7.

Teacher: Which rule did she work on first?

Isabel: She did the total.

Teacher: So she didn't use any color yet. She wrote the equation and made sure she had the right total. What did you do next Emilia?

Emilia circles the 6 of her equation with red and the 1 with blue.

Teacher: What did Emilia do after she wrote the equation?

Toshi: She circled the 6 with red and then the 1 with blue.

Teacher: Why?

Toshi: She needed the bigger number to be red.

Emilia continues to solve the problem. She writes 5 + 2 = 7 in black and circles the 5 with red and the 2 with blue. Then she writes 4 + 3 = 7 in black and circles the 4 with red and the 3 with blue.

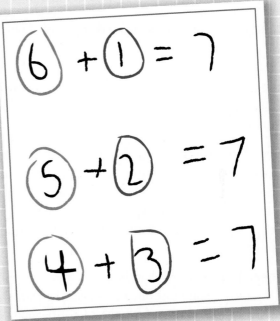

Emilia's Work

Teacher: Who can explain Emilia's strategy?

Sacha: First she writes equations. Then she circles them with the right color.

Bruce: I got the same ones. So I think there's only 3 ways.

Leah: What about 7 red and 0 blue?

Students have disagreed about 7 + 0 and 0 + 7 as they worked on How Many of Each? problems. The teacher decides to revisit this ongoing question.

Teacher: Let's talk about that. Is it OK to have 7 reds and 0 blues?

Isabel: There has to be *some* blues or else it won't work. It just doesn't seem right. The teacher needs blues and reds.

Jacinta: It won't work because it says more reds and there has to be blue too.

Nicky: It doesn't say that in the problem.

Stacy: We can't have 7 red and 0 blue because then we have no blue and the paper says that you need blue.

Teacher: How does the paper say that you need blue?

Stacy: You have *some* blue.

Teacher: And is 0 some? *(No)* So we can agree that 7 red and 0 blue does not work as a solution because it doesn't fit both of the rules? *(Yes)*

Happy that students are using the meaning of the words in the problem to argue their case, the teacher now returns to an earlier comment. She encourages students to compare 2 students' strategies, and to explain how the solutions in one form (e.g., equations) match solutions in another form (e.g., cube towers).

Teacher: Bruce guessed that there are only 3 solutions for this puzzle and I saw other kids agreeing with him. Bruce, why do you think that? I notice you have some towers.

Bruce: First I made equations out of these. Then I made towers.

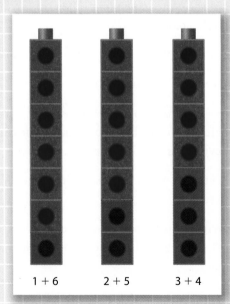

1 + 6   2 + 5   3 + 4

Teacher: Let's take a look at Bruce's towers. [She places them in the middle of the circle near Emilia's paper.] Bruce's first tower had 6 reds and 1 blue. Which of Emilia's equations is that?

Vic: The first one, 6 + 1.

Teacher: And here's Bruce's second tower, 5 + 2. 5 what?

Isabel: 5 red and 2 blue.

Vic: The next one is going to have 3.

Sacha: It's a staircase.

Teacher: Is he right, does the next one have 3? *(Yes)* What's the equation for this tower? *(4 + 3 = 7)* So one way to think about this is that Bruce's towers make a picture of Emilia's what?

Leah: Equations.

Teacher: Do all of the equations work for this problem?

The teacher has students check that each solution fits both rules. The class agrees that all of the solutions fit the rules.

Teacher: Do we have all of the ways to solve this problem? Are there any other ways to solve this problem?

Diego: Since there has to be 7 crayons, we have all the ways because we can't go over 6 for the red.

Libby: Mine's the opposite of Diego's. Yes, because you can't go under 4 red because then we would have more blue than red and that doesn't fit the rule.

Teacher: What number can't we go under for blue?

Libby: One.

Isabel: We have all the ways because there's a 1, 2, 3, 4, 5, and 6 and we can't go over 6 because that would be 7 and then we'd have no blues.

This teacher is pleased that several students are ready to reason about this question in such a sophisticated way. She also knows that, for many of her first graders, just solving such a crayon puzzle and recording their work is an appropriately challenging task.

Dialogue Box

An Addition Story Problem Aloud

In the previous session, this class was introduced to the routine for solving story problems aloud as a group. Today, the class solves another problem together, and, for the first time, the teacher models some ways to record the students' strategies for solving the problem.

Teacher: I have a story that I am going to share with you. Listen carefully. Then I am going to call on some students to retell the story. Here we go. *Kylie and Koni were on a rock hunt. Kylie found 4 smooth rocks. Koni found 5 bumpy rocks.* [She reads this story aloud to the class, twice.] Raise your hand if you can tell that story to the class.

Stacy: Kylie and Koni went to find rocks. Kylie found 4 smooth rocks and Koni found 5 bumpy rocks.

Felipe: Kylie and Koni went on rock hunt. Kylie found 4 smooth rocks, Koni found 5 bumpy rocks.

Teacher: OK, I'm going to read it again and I want you to close your eyes while I'm reading it and make a movie of it in your head. [She rereads the story.] OK, now open your eyes and I have a question for you. How many rocks did they find? I don't want you to tell me the answer; tell me how you figured out the answer.

Keena: I put 4 on my fingers [holds up 4 fingers] then I added 5, 6, 7, 8, 9 [holds up one finger for each additional number].

The teacher models Keena's strategy with her hands and then draws a face with an open mouth and hands that are holding up 9 fingers.

Teacher: OK, so here's Keena and she has an open mouth because she talks to solve this and her answer is 9 rocks.

Teacher: Raise your hand if that was your strategy. [Six students raise their hands and the teacher writes their initials under the drawing.] Who can share a different strategy that they used?

Paula: I put up 4 fingers, then I put up 5 fingers and I counted them all together.

Teacher: OK, so that's a little bit different. [She holds up 4 fingers, then 5 fingers and has Paula count them.] So you have 9 what?

Paula: Rocks.

The teacher draws a girl with an open mouth, and 4 fingers and then 5 fingers, and then numbers the fingers 1–9.

Teacher: How is Paula's strategy different from Keena's?

Keena: Because she put them up and then counted them all together. But I didn't. I went 4; 5, 6, 7, 8, 9.

Teacher: If you did it Paula's way, raise your hand. [Four students raise their hands.] Does anybody have a totally different way?

Vic: I didn't use my hands at all. I thought and I saw 5 smooth rocks and 4 bumpy rocks at the top and I counted the 4 bumpy rocks and the 5 smooth rocks and I put them altogether and I counted them up and it equaled 9.

The teacher draws a boy with his mouth closed and a thought bubble with 9 rocks in it, which are numbered 1 to 9.

Teacher: Who did it Vic's way? [Two students raise their hands.] Vic's way reminds me of Paula's way. See? They both showed 4, showed 5, and *counted them all*. I even wrote all of the same numbers! But Paula used her fingers and Vic used rocks. Anybody have another way?

Libby: I did 5 plus 4. I did 5; 6, 7, 8, 9.

Teacher: Did you use your fingers like Keena? [She points to the drawing of Keena's strategy.]

Libby: Yeah.

Teacher: Which way is most like Libby's?

Nicky: Keena's because she did 4 and she did 5.

Teacher: Right they both used the same idea, but they started with different numbers. Keena counted on from 4—and Libby counted on from 5. These are all awesome ways to solve the problem. Tomorrow we are going to do some more work with this.

Notice how, even this early in first grade, this teacher encourages students to compare their own strategies with those of their classmates ("How is Paula's strategy different from Keena's?" and "Which way is most like Libby's?") and helps them do so ("Vic's way reminds me of Paula's" and "Keena counted on from 4, and Libby counted on from 5"). Discussions like this one help take different strategies for (in this case) adding two numbers and make them public and explicit for all to think about and possibly try. They encourage students to listen to and learn from one another and set the stage for discussions about strategies and efficiency that will unfold over the year.

A Subtraction Story Problem Aloud

Students have recently been introduced to subtraction story problems. Notice how this teacher connects students back to the context, describes strategies, and models the strategies on paper and with various tools. He also encourages students to listen to one another, and to think about and compare a variety of strategies, including ones other than their own.

Teacher: I'm going to tell you another story. Remember that your job is to listen and try to picture it in your mind. My story today is about a girl named Libby and a boy named Jonah. Libby is working at the art table, and she has 10 crayons. Picture it, do you see it? Jonah goes over to the art table, and Libby is really, really generous and gives Jonah 4 crayons. Who can retell that story?

Danielle: Wait, how many did she have?

Another student is worried that he missed the names of the students. The teacher reassures them, and then retells the story. He asks for volunteers to retell it in their own words.

Keena: Libby was sitting at the art table. She had 10 crayons. Jonah went over to the art table, and Libby was really generous and gave Jonah 4 crayons.

Vic: Libby went to the art table, and Libby had 10 crayons, and Jonah came over, and Libby was really, really nice and gave him 4 crayons.

Teacher: Does Libby have more than 10 crayons or fewer than 10?

Carol: Less because she is giving them away.

Marta: Less because Jonah took 4 and that's 6.

Teacher: So you're thinking of the answer, and that's less than 10?

Marta: Yes.

The teacher uses this comment to transition to asking all students to solve the problem. He rereads the story and invites students to use the cubes in the center of the rug. He gives them some time to work and, when students seem to have finished, asks them to share strategies.

Carol: I took my hands and holded up 10 hands, I mean fingers, and then I took away 4, and then I counted the ones up, and I got 6.

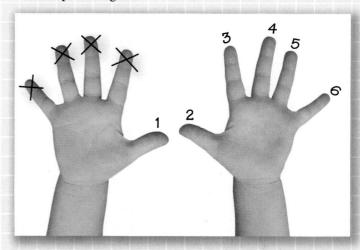

Teacher: Carol held up 10 fingers [demonstrates this strategy]. What did her fingers stand for? (*the crayons*) Then she took away 4, and counted the fingers that were left. Did anyone do something similar to Carol?

Richard: I did [holds up 5 fingers on each hand]. 5 and 5 make 10 and take away 4 [puts down 4 fingers on one hand], leaves this [shows the remaining fingers], and 1 and 5 make 6.

Teacher: Interesting. Could you show your idea with cubes?

Richard makes 2 towers of 5 cubes, takes off 4 from one tower, and puts the remaining cubes into a single tower of 6.

Neil: I did it with cubes too. I built a 10 [shows a tower of 10], then take away 4 [breaks off 4]. Six are left— 1, 2, 3, 4, 5, 6.

Teacher: Can someone tell us what Neil did?

Allie: He took out 10 cubes and then took 4 away, and then he counted how many were left.

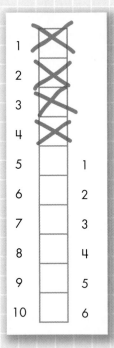

Teacher: OK, who has another way of solving the problem?

Marta: I counted backward with my fingers. I started with 9.

Teacher: And how did you know when to stop?

Marta: When I got to 4.

Leah: Why did you start with 9?

Talisa: Yeah, shouldn't you start with 10?

Marta: I put up 4 fingers and I counted them backward until I had none up.

Teacher: What did you say when you put down one finger?

Marta: 9.

Paula: You pretend 10 isn't there and you go 9, 8, 7. . . .

Teacher: What is Marta pretending these 4 fingers are?

Chris: The 4 crayons Libby gave to Jonah.

Teacher: So if Libby had 10 and gives one to Jonah, how many does she have left?

Leah: 9. Oh! That's why the first number you said was 9. It's after you take away the first crayon.

The teacher records Marta's strategy as she described it, but he also models it on the class number line, in writing and aloud, thinking that seeing the jumps might help more students have access to Marta's strategy.

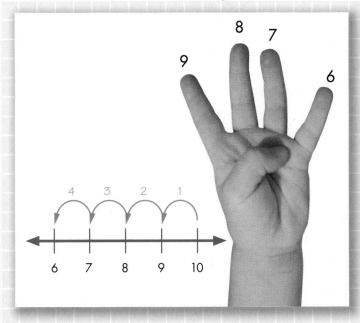

Teacher: Two people used their fingers today. Carol showed all 10 crayons on her fingers, then took away 4, and counted how many fingers were left. Raise your hand if you used your fingers like Carol. Raise your hand if you counted backward on your fingers like Marta did.

Discussing Addition Strategies

The challenge for any teacher is to figure out what strategies students are using currently and how successful they are in using them. With a sense of this, the question becomes how to move students toward more efficient strategies without pushing them into using a strategy by rote that they are not yet ready to understand and therefore cannot yet use meaningfully.

One thing that helps students try, and eventually adopt, new strategies for adding, is having many opportunities to hear a variety of strategies named, described, and modeled. There are many ways that you can build these opportunities into your math class, as you talk with students at work, and during whole class discussions. Consider the following examples:

This teacher is introducing Roll and Record *to the class by playing a game with a partner. Notice how she very briefly and naturally models a strategy that she has seen at least one student in the class using. She is not teaching students how to count on. She is sharing counting on as one possible way to add two numbers, expecting only those who are able to make sense of it to use it.*

Teacher: I rolled 5 and 3. So now I need to add those numbers together. I'd like to show you something that Emilia does when she adds. She starts with the higher number, 5, and then she counts, 6, 7, 8 [points to the 3 dots on the other dot cube]. So I am going to write an 8 in the box above the 8 on my paper. William, your turn.

This teacher is discussing a Math Workshop in which Double Compare *and games that involved adding two dot cubes were available. Notice how she helps students name and record the strategies they are using.*

Teacher: When you were playing *Double Compare, Roll and Record,* or *Five-in-a-Row,* how did you figure out how many you had?

Bruce: When we played, Chris thought he had a taller number than I did. He said "Me" but I said, wait, maybe you don't. So we counted and he had 14 and I had 19.

Teacher: Double-checking is always a good idea. Who has another idea?

Lyle: If you memorize it then you don't have to count. Like 3, you can say 3 and don't have to count it and if the other card is 4, you could just say 3. 4, 5, 6, 7.

The teacher sketches two cards showing 3 and 4. She labels the pictures on the 4 card 4, 5, 6, and 7.

Teacher: So you did something called *counting on.* What are some other ways we could add 3 and 4? [She displays cards and dot cubes, each showing 3 and 4.]

Isabel: First count 3, then count 4. 1, 2, 3, 4, 5, 6, 7. [She counts each dot on the dot cube].

The teacher draws dot pictures of 4 and 3, and labels each dot with a number.

Teacher: Who else *counted all* of the dots or pictures? Who used a different way?

Nicky: I did it sort of the same as Isabel, but I used my fingers. [The teacher has Nicky come up to chart paper. She traces three fingers of one hand and four of the other. She puts a number inside each finger.]

Diego: I saw 3 and 3. I knew 3 and 3 is 6, so 3 and 4 is 1 more. That's 7.

Teacher: All right, Diego used a *doubles combination* that he knows: 3 and 3 are 6. He used that to help him with 3 + 4.

She models Diego's thinking on the chart paper with 2 equations:

$$3 + 3 = 6$$
$$3 + 4 = 7$$

Chris: I just know that 3 and 4, that makes 7.

Felipe: You could do 4, 5, 6, 7.

Teacher: What Felipe did, that's called *counting on,* just like Lyle's. [She records Felipe's way underneath Lyle's.] There are many different ways to add, so I am making this chart to remind us all of the different ways we came up with.

This class is discussing Double Compare. *They have turned over a 9 and a 6 and now are sharing ways to add those numbers. Notice how the teacher helps students name and describe the strategies and how she decides to delay the discussion of a strategy that she knows all but a few students are not ready to grapple with.*

Teacher: What are some ways I can add these two numbers?

Edgar: [points to the 9 card] 9. [Then he points to each object on the 6 card as he counts on.] 10, 11, 12, 13, 14, 15.

Tamika: You can start with 6 and then count the same way. [She demonstrates.] 7, 8, 9, 10, 11, 12, 13, 14, 15.

Leah: You can also count each thing by 1. [Leah demonstrates.]

Teacher: So far we've gotten 15 all three times. Edgar started at 9 and *counted up* 6, Tamika started at 6 and *counted up* 9, and Leah *counted everything* and they all got 15.

Teo: I think it's supposed to be 16.

Neil: No, it's not 16 because, well, you use 1 up from 10 and that takes away from the teens. So subtracting 1 equals it to be 15.

Teacher: If that's confusing to other first graders, you might not want to use that way, but it is something to think more about.

Stacy: I think it's 15 because let's say this is a 10 and this is a 6. It would be 16 but 9 is 1 less than 10, so the answer is 1 less than 16 and that's 15.

Teacher: So you were thinking kind of what Neil was thinking. Let's flip over Sacha's cards [0 and 5]. What do you do with a zero?

Leah: Just don't count it. So Sacha has 5.

Naming and Comparing Strategies for Subtracting

The challenge for any teacher is to figure out what strategies students are using currently, and how successful they are in using them. With a sense of this, the question becomes how to move students toward more efficient strategies without pushing them into rotely using a strategy they are not yet ready to understand and therefore cannot yet use meaningfully.

One thing that helps students try, and eventually adopt, new strategies for adding and subtracting is having many opportunities to hear a variety of strategies named, described, and modeled. There are many ways that you can build these opportunities into your math class as you talk with students at work and during whole-class discussions. Consider the following subtraction examples. A similar **Dialogue Box** about addition strategies can be found on page 183.

Students in this class were sharing strategies for solving the following problem.

Paul picked 12 apples. He gave 6 of them to Rosa. How many apples did Paul have then?

Teacher: Who has a strategy they'd like to share?

Nicky: I used the cubes and I took 12, and I moved 6 to the other side, and I counted how many I had left.

Teacher: Can anybody show what Nicky did to solve this problem?

Keena: [counts out 12 cubes] She put them all in a group, and then she moved 6 to the other side [breaks off 6 and moves them aside], and then she counted how many she had left: 1, 2, 3, 4, 5, 6.

Teacher: So Nicky counted 12, broke off 6, and counted the ones that were left. Did anyone else *count all* of the apples, then take 6 away and count how many were left? [A few hands go up.]

Notice how the teacher asks another student to demonstrate Nicky's strategy with cubes, and how she describes and asks students to think about whether this sounds like the way they solved the problem.

Neil: I used my fingers and 2 of Felipe's fingers. Here's 12. Take away 1, 2, 3, 4, 5, 6 [puts a finger down for each number he says]. Now we have 5 [waves one hand], 6.

Teacher: So Neil used a different tool. Nicky used cubes, but Neil used fingers. They both showed all 12 apples, then took away 6, then counted how many were left.

The teacher acknowledges that Neil and Nicky used different tools to solve the problem, but encourages students to compare the strategies and think about what is similar about them.

Teacher: Did anybody else use their fingers as a tool?

Tamika: I did, but I did it different. I thought I have to take away 6 apples. 11 [raises one finger], 10 [raises a second finger], 9 [raises a third], 8 [raises a fourth], 7 [raises a fifth], 6 [raises a sixth].

Teacher: Did you hear how Tamika *counted back,* just like we do sometimes in *Start With/Get To*? Each time she said a new number, she put up a finger. [The teacher asks Tamika to demonstrate again, and points to the numbers said aloud on the number line as she does so.] Tamika, how did you know when to stop?

As this student uses her fingers to count back, the teacher keeps track of the numbers she says on the number line.

Tamika: When I had 6 fingers up.

Teacher: How did you know to stop at 6?

Tamika: Because I had to take away 6 apples.

When counting back to solve a subtraction problem, keeping track can get complicated. Students must simultaneously keep track of the numbers they are counting down (11, 10, 9, 8, 7, 6) and the number of numbers counted (1, 2, 3, 4, 5, 6). The teacher has Tamika demonstrate a second time, and connects what Tamika is

doing to a familiar activity, *Start With/Get To.* She also models a way for students to see both counts at the same time on the number line. Modeling such a strategy as jumps on a number line can help students make sense of why the first number Tamika says when she counts is 11, not the 12 that is in the problem.

William: I just know that 6 and 6 is 12. So if you have 12 and you take away 6, it's 6.

Teacher: William knows about *doubles.* He said he knows 6 plus 6, and that helped him know that 12 take away 6 is 6. Did anyone solve it another way?

Discussions throughout this unit aim to make strategies for adding and subtracting public and explicit. Note that students are likely to initially see counting all with cubes as a different strategy than counting all with their fingers or drawing and counting pictures of all the parts of a problem. The discussions in this and future units encourage students to think not only about how these strategies are different but also about how they are similar (i.e., these children showed all of the apples, took away the 6 apples, and then counted how many were left).

As students become more familiar with the various methods for solving problems and have experience with these kinds of discussions, they will be better able to name their own strategies and compare them with those of their classmates.

Does This Show Paula's Strategy?

Many teachers say that helping students find ways to record their math work is a big focus in Grade 1. Particularly challenging is helping students show the strategy they actually used, rather than one that is easy to show on paper. In addition to modeling, here are a variety of strategies teachers have used.

From the very start, this teacher encourages students to think about whether the way she records students' strategies feels like what they actually did to solve the problem.

Teacher: OK, let's remember our story. [reads the following story.]

I gave 8 worms to Lele, our frog and she ate 3. Now I'd like to know how many worms are left.

Teacher: Who has a strategy they'd like to share?

Lyle: I had 8 cubes.

Teacher: And what do those cubes stand for? In the story, there were 8 . . .

Lyle: Worms. Then take off 3, for the ones Lele ate, and that makes 5.

The teacher draws a cube tower of 8. She crosses out the top 3 cubes.

Teacher: Does this show what you did, Lyle?

Lyle: Well, on my paper, I had numbers.

Teacher: It sounds like you were clearer than I was. Could you come up and add the numbers you used to our chart?

A student uses a picture to show how he solved a subtraction story problem.

When such a habit is established, students will feel more and more comfortable making suggestions about other students' work (i.e., "I can't tell what your answer is.") and even analyzing whether the teacher's recording accurately reflects someone else's strategy.

Now these students are discussing the following story problem:

Jake and Louisa were playing with the Geoblocks. Jake had 4 blocks. Louisa had 5 blocks. They worked together to make a building with all of the blocks. How many blocks did they use?

Teacher: Who has another strategy they'd like to share?

Paula: I know 4 plus 4 is 8. 4 and 5 is 1 more, so it's 9.

When representing this strategy, the teacher purposefully decides to record in a way that does not reflect what Paula said. She draws a group of 4 things, a group of 5 things, and then numbers the things from 1 to 9.

Teacher: Does this show Paula's strategy? Is this what she did? No? What should I write?

These students are familiar with the routine for solving story problems and sharing solutions. They have seen many different models for recording. Also, the classroom culture is such that students are used to listening to one another, repeating someone else's strategy, and commenting on someone else's work.

This is the problem the class discusses next:

Paul picked 12 apples. He gave 6 of them to Rosa. How many apples did Paul have then?

Teacher: OK, let's listen to Libby, and then I'm going to ask someone to explain what she did.

Libby: I drew 12 dots, then I circled 6 and then I counted the ones that weren't circled.

Teacher: Paul, can you do what Libby did right up here?

Paul draws 12 dots in a row on the chart paper, circles 6 dots, and numbers the noncircled dots.

Teacher: Do you think that shows what Libby did? (agreement from the class)

Libby: Actually I drew the dots like dice—6 and 6. But I didn't say that before.

Paul listens to Libby and picks the marker up again. This time he draws 2 groups of 6 dots, just like on dot cubes.

Paul: Like this? (Libby nods.) Then did you just cross out one whole dot cube? (Libby nods, and Paul proceeds.)

When students are comfortable looking at a variety of student work, they can be challenged to say how a student solved the problem, judging from their recording sheet.

Teacher: I have a paper here for this problem (reads the problem):

Kim had 7 toy cars. Sam had 6 toy cars. How many toy cars did they have altogether?

Sample Student Work

Teacher: Who has an idea about *how* this person solved the problem? Do you think this person counted every single car?

Student Math Handbook

The *Student Math Handbook* pages related to this unit are pictured on the following pages. This book is designed to be used flexibly: as a resource for students doing classwork, as a book students can take home for reference while doing homework and playing math games with their families, and as a reference for families to better understand the work their children are doing in class.

When students take the *Student Math Handbook* home, they and their families can discuss these pages together to reinforce or enhance students' understanding of the mathematical concepts and games in this unit.

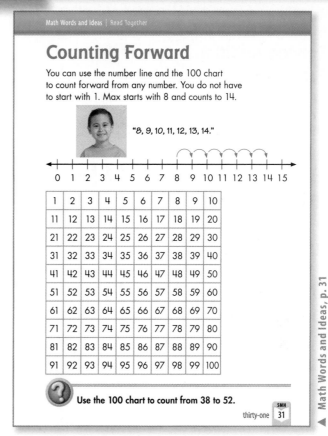

Math Words and Ideas, p. 31

Math Words and Ideas | Read Together

Counting Forward

You can use the number line and the 100 chart to count forward from any number. You do not have to start with 1. Max starts with 8 and counts to 14.

"8, 9, 10, 11, 12, 13, 14."

Use the 100 chart to count from 38 to 52.

thirty-one **SMH 31**

Math Words and Ideas, p. 33

Math Words and Ideas | Read Together

Solving Addition Problems (page 1 of 5)

Here is a story problem:

Kim has 3 crayons. Sam gives her 4 more. How many crayons does Kim have now?

Does Kim have more crayons at the beginning or the end of the story?

thirty-three **SMH 33**

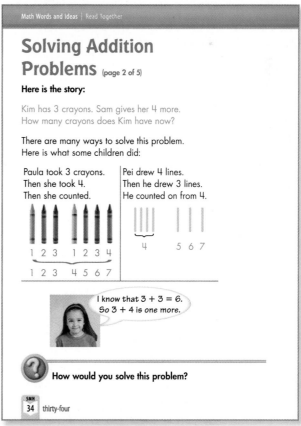

Math Words and Ideas, p. 34

Math Words and Ideas | Read Together

Solving Addition Problems (page 2 of 5)

Here is the story:

Kim has 3 crayons. Sam gives her 4 more. How many crayons does Kim have now?

There are many ways to solve this problem. Here is what some children did:

Paula took 3 crayons. Then she took 4. Then she counted.

1 2 3 1 2 3 4
1 2 3 4 5 6 7

Pei drew 4 lines. Then he drew 3 lines. He counted on from 4.

4   5 6 7

I know that 3 + 3 = 6. So 3 + 4 is one more.

How would you solve this problem?

SMH 34 thirty-four

Solving Addition Problems (page 3 of 5)

Math Words
- equation
- plus
- equal to
- addend
- sum
- equal sign

Kim has 3 crayons. Sam gives her 4 more.
Now Kim has 7 crayons.

Here are 2 equations for this problem.

3 + 4 = 7

3 plus 4 is equal to 7.

7 = 3 + 4

7 is equal to 3 plus 4.

3 and 4 are the addends. 7 is the total, or the sum.

The equal sign shows that 3 + 4 is the same amount as 7.

thirty-five **35**

Math Words and Ideas, p. 35

Solving Addition Problems (page 4 of 5)

Here is a story problem:

Rosa has 8 shells.
Sam gives her 3 more shells.
Max gives her 2 more shells.
How many shells does Rosa have now?

 Does Rosa have more shells at the beginning or at the end of the story?

36 thirty-six

Math Words and Ideas, p. 36

Solving Addition Problems (page 5 of 5)

There are many ways to solve this problem.
This is what some children did:

Paul drew and counted each shell.

Isabel counted on from 8 on a number line.

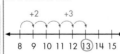

8 9 10 11 12 (13) 14 15

Vic used a combination of 10.

8 + 2 = 10

Then he counted on.

11, 12, 13

I know that
2 + 3 = 5.
Then, I count on
6, 7, 8, 9, 10,
11, 12, 13.

 How would you solve the problem?

thirty-seven **37**

Math Words and Ideas, p. 37

Solving Subtraction Problems (page 1 of 5)

Here is a story problem:

Sam had 10 pennies.
He spent 6 on a pencil.
How many pennies did he have left?

 Does Sam have more pennies at the beginning of the story or at the end?

38 thirty-eight

Math Words and Ideas, p. 38

Top-left panel

Solving Subtraction Problems (page 2 of 5)

There are many ways to solve this problem.
This is what some children did.

Kim drew 10 circles and crossed out 6. Then she counted how many were left.

Vic counted back 6 on a number line.

Max counted up from 6 to 10.

Then he counted his fingers:
1, 2, 3, 4

Rosa used what she knew about addition combinations.

I know that 4 + 6 = 10. So, 10 − 6 must be 4.

How would you solve the problem?

◀ Math Words and Ideas, p. 39

Top-right panel

Solving Subtraction Problems (page 3 of 5)

Math Words
• minus
• equals
• difference

Sam had 10 pennies.
He spent 6 on a pencil.
Now he has 4.

Here is an equation for this problem.

$$10 - 6 = 4$$

10 minus 6 equals 4

The difference between 10 and 6 is 4.

The equal sign shows that 10 − 6 is the same amount as 4.

◀ Math Words and Ideas, p. 40

Bottom-left panel

Solving Subtraction Problems (page 4 of 5)

Here is a story problem.

Max had 15 pennies in his piggy bank. He took out 7 pennies to buy a pencil. How many pennies are still in his piggy bank?

Does Max have more pennies in his bank at the beginning of the story or at the end?

◀ Math Words and Ideas, p. 41

Bottom-right panel

Solving Subtraction Problems (page 5 of 5)

Max had 15 pennies in his piggy bank.
He took out 7 pennies to buy a pencil.
How many pennies are still in his piggy bank?

There are many ways to solve this problem.
This is what some children did.

Tina counted out 15 and took 7 away. Then she counted how many were left.

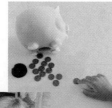

Stacy used a number line and counted back.

Leah counted up from 7 to 15. It was 8.

Paul used what he knew about addition combinations.

If 7 + 7 = 14, then 7 + 8 = 15. So, 15 − 7 = 8.

How would you solve the problem?

◀ Math Words and Ideas, p. 42

Using Math Symbols
(page 1 of 2)

+ plus sign addition sign	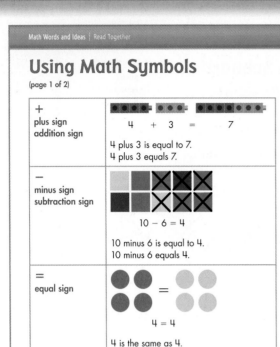 4 + 3 = 7 4 plus 3 is equal to 7. 4 plus 3 equals 7.
− minus sign subtraction sign	$10 - 6 = 4$ 10 minus 6 is equal to 4. 10 minus 6 equals 4.
= equal sign	$4 = 4$ 4 is the same as 4. 4 is equal to 4. 4 equals 4.

▲ Math Words and Ideas, p. 44

Using Math Symbols
(page 2 of 2)

Math Words
• **equation**

An equation uses numbers and symbols to show what is happening in a math problem.

$8 + 2 = 10$ $10 - 4 = 6$

Here are two ways to write addition or subtraction problems.

$$\begin{array}{r} 8 \\ + 2 \\ \hline 10 \end{array}$$ is the same as $8 + 2 = 10$

$10 - 4 = 6$ is the same as $$\begin{array}{r} 10 \\ - 4 \\ \hline 6 \end{array}$$

▲ Math Words and Ideas, p. 45

How Many of Each? (page 1 of 2)

Here is a story problem.

I have 6 vegetables.
Some are peas.
Some are carrots.
How many of each could I have?
How many peas? How many carrots?

There are many different solutions.

Here is one.

I could have   2 carrots   and   4 peas.

     $6 = \quad 2 \quad + \quad 4$

 Can you find other combinations of peas and carrots?

▲ Math Words and Ideas, p. 46

How Many of Each? (page 2 of 2)

Here are some children's solutions.

Edgar: 5 peas and 1 carrot $5 + 1 = 6$	Allie: 3 peas and 3 carrots $3 + 3 = 6$
Nicky: 2 peas and 4 carrots $2 + 4 = 6$	Talisa: 4 peas and 2 carrots $4 + 2 = 6$

Lyle: 1 pea and 5 carrots

$1 + 5 = 6$

 If there were 7 vegetables, how many peas and carrots could there be? Find as many combinations as you can.

▲ Math Words and Ideas, p. 47

Combinations of 10 (page 1 of 2)

Here are some ways to make 10.

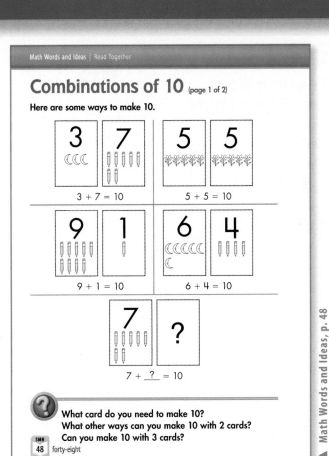

3 + 7 = 10

5 + 5 = 10

9 + 1 = 10

6 + 4 = 10

7 + ___ = 10

What card do you need to make 10?
What other ways can you make 10 with 2 cards?
Can you make 10 with 3 cards?

SMH 48 forty-eight

▲ Math Words and Ideas, p. 48

Combinations of 10 (page 2 of 2)

0 + 10 = 10
1 + 9 = 10
2 + 8 = 10
3 + 7 = 10
4 + 6 = 10
5 + 5 = 10
6 + 4 = 10
7 + 3 = 10
8 + 2 = 10
9 + 1 = 10
10 + 0 = 10

What do you notice about these combinations of 10?

forty-nine **SMH 49**

▲ Math Words and Ideas, p. 49

Counters in a Cup

You need

- 8–12 counters
- cup
- recording sheet

Play with a partner.

1. Decide how many counters to play with. Both players write this number on their recording sheets.
2. Count out that many counters.
3. Player 1 hides some of the counters under a cup.
4. Player 2 tells how many are hidden.
5. Player 1 removes the cup.
6. Both players count the counters that were under the cup and record that number.
7. Keep playing with the same set of counters. Take turns being Player 1 and Player 2.
8. The game is over when the grid is full.

SMH G4

▲ Gamess, G4

Dot Addition

You need

- deck of Dot Addition Cards
- 3 gameboards (one per player and one to play on)

Play with a partner.

1. Deal 4 rows of 5 cards, with the dots facing up.
2. Player 1 finds cards that combine to make one of the numbers on the gameboard.
3. Both players record the combination.
4. Player 2 finds cards that combine to make another number on the gameboard.
5. Both players record the combination.
6. The game is over when the gameboard is full.

More Ways to Play

- Play with different gameboards.
- Use each card only once.
- Play again, with the same gameboard. Try to find a different way to make each number.

SMH G5

▲ Games, G5

Five-in-a-Row: Subtraction

You need

- 7–12 number cube
- dot cube
- 20 counters
- gameboard

Play with a partner. Work together.

1. Player 1 rolls two cubes.

2. Player 1 subtracts the smaller number from the larger number.

3. Player 1 covers that number on the gameboard.

4. Player 2 takes a turn, following steps 1–3.

5. If the number is already covered, roll again.

6. The game is over when all of the numbers in one row are covered. The numbers can go across ▢▢▢▢▢, down ▯, or corner to corner.

SMH
G10

▲ Games, G10

Five-in-a-Row with Three Cards

You need

- deck of Primary Number Cards (without Wild Cards)
- 20 counters
- gameboard

Play with a partner. Work together.

1. Turn over the top 3 cards.

2. Player 1 chooses a sum to cover on the gameboard. Choose any sum you can make with 2 of the numbers.
   $3 + 7 = ⑩$ $7 + 1 = ⑧$ $3 + 1 = ④$

3. Turn over three more cards.

4. Player 2 chooses a sum to cover on the gameboard.

5. Keep playing. If all of the sums are covered, pick 3 new cards.

6. The game is over when all of the numbers in one row are covered. The numbers can go across ▢▢▢▢▢, down ▯, or corner to corner.

More Ways to Play

- Play with different gameboards.
- Play with the Wild Cards. A Wild Card can be any number.
- Turn over 5 cards on each turn. Choose any sum you can make with 2 of the numbers.

SMH
G11

▲ Games, G11

How Many Am I Hiding?

You need

- 8–12 connecting cubes
- recording sheet

Play with a partner.

1. Decide how many cubes to play with. Both players write this number on their recording sheets.

2. Make a tower with that many cubes.

3. Player 1 hides some of the cubes.

4. Player 2 tells how many cubes are hidden.

5. Player 1 shows the hidden cubes.

6. Both players count how many were hidden and then record that number on their recording sheets.

7. Keep playing with the same tower. Take turns being Player 1 and Player 2.

8. The game is over when the grid is full.

More Ways to Play

- Play with 5 cubes of one color and 5 cubes of another color.

SMH
G14

▲ Games, G14

Make 10

You need

- deck of Primary Number Cards (without Wild Cards)
- blank sheet of paper

Play with a partner.

1. Deal 4 rows of 5 cards, with the numbers showing.

2. Player 1 finds two cards that make 10. Player 1 takes the cards and records the combination of 10.

3. Replace the missing cards with 2 cards from the deck.

4. Player 2 finds two cards that make 10. Player 2 takes the cards and records the combination of 10.

5. Replace the missing cards.

6. Keep taking turns finding two cards that make 10 and recording.

7. The game is over when there are no more cards or there are no more cards that make 10.

More Ways to Play

- Play with the Wild Cards. A Wild Card can be any number.
- Replace the cards *only* when there are no more pairs that make 10.
- Find more than 2 cards that make 10.

SMH
G15

▲ Games, G15

Roll and Record: Subtraction

You need

- 7–12 number cube
- dot cube
- recording sheet

Play alone.

1 Roll the 2 cubes.

2 Subtract the smaller number from the larger number. $6 - \square$

3 Record the answer on the recording sheet.

4 The game is over when one column is full.

◀ Games, G20

Tens Go Fish

You need

- deck of Primary Number Cards (without Wild Cards)
- sheet of paper

Play with a partner.

1 Each player is dealt 5 cards from the Primary Number Card deck.

2 Each player looks for pairs from his or her cards that make 10. Players put down the pairs of cards that make 10, and they draw new cards to replace them from the Primary Number Card deck.

3 Players take turns asking each other for a card that will make 10 with a card in their own hands.

If a player gets the card, he or she puts the pair down and picks a new card from the deck.

If a player does not get the card, the player must "Go fish" and pick a new card from the deck.

If the new card from the deck makes 10 with a card in the player's hand, he or she puts the pair of cards down and takes another card.

If a player runs out of cards, the player picks two new cards. A player's turn is over when no more pairs can be made that make 10.

4 The game is over when there are no more cards.

5 At the end of the game, players record their combinations of 10.

◀ Games, G23

Three Towers of 10

You need

- dot cube
- 30 connecting cubes per player, in 2 colors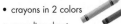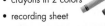
- crayons in 2 colors
- recording sheet

Play with a partner. Work together.

1 Each player picks a color of cubes.

2 Player 1 rolls and makes a tower with that many cubes.

3 Player 2 rolls and takes that many cubes.

4 Player 2 adds the cubes to the tower. A tower can have only 10 cubes. Start a new tower with any extra cubes.

5 The game is over when there are 3 towers of 10 cubes.

6 Both players record. Show how many cubes of each color there are in each tower. Write an equation for each tower.

More Ways to Play

- Make 5 towers of 10.
- Make 3 towers of 15.
- Play with 2 dot cubes.
- Play with 1 dot cube and 1 number cube.
- Play with 2 number cubes.

◀ Games, G25

Index

V

Venn diagrams, 69, 81
Vocabulary
  add, 103
  combination, 65
  combine, 40
  count all, 124
  count back, 121
  count on, 113
  count up, 121
  equal sign, 29
  equation, 27
  fewer, 37
  minus, 108
  more, 37, 77
  plus sign, 41
  story problems, 37
  sum, 103
  ten-frame, 46

W

Writing opportunities, 14

Z

Zero
  as an addend, 74, 174, 177–178